FUNDAMENTALS
OF SMART
CONTRACT
SECURITY

FUNDAMENTALS OF SMART CONTRACT SECURITY

RICHARD MA, JAN GORZNY,
EDWARD ZULKOSKI, KACPER BAK,
AND OLGA V. MACK

FOREWORD BY
KEISUKE HONDA

MOMENTUM PRESS
ENGINEERING

MOMENTUM PRESS, LLC, NEW YORK

Fundamentals of Smart Contract Security

First published by Momentum Press®, LLC
222 East 46th Street, New York, NY 10017
www.momentumpress.net

ISBN-13: 978-1-94944-936-5 (print)
ISBN-13: 978-1-94944-937-2 (e-book)

Momentum Press Computer Engineering Foundations, Currents, and Trajectories Collection

Cover and interior design by Exeter Premedia Services Private Ltd., Chennai, India

10 9 8 7 6 5 4 3 2 1

Printed in the United States of America

To the pioneering spirit.

ABSTRACT

Smart contracts are an innovative application of blockchain technology. Acting as decentralized custodians of digital assets, they allow us to transfer value and information more effectively by reducing the need to trust a third party.

By eliminating the need for intermediaries, smart contracts have the potential to massively scale the world economy and unleash the potential for faster and more efficient solutions than traditional systems could ever provide.

But there's one catch: while blockchains are secure, smart contracts are not.

Security vulnerabilities in smart contracts have led to over $250 million USD in value to be lost or stolen. For smart contract technology to achieve its full potential, these security vulnerabilities need to be addressed.

Written by security experts at the forefront of this dynamic industry, this book teaches state-of-the-art smart contract security principles and practices.

Help us secure the future of blockchain technology and join us at the forefront today!

KEYWORDS

blockchain; smart contracts; smart contracts law; security; cybersecurity; DLT; distributed ledger technology; Ethereum; cryptocurrencies; bitcoin; fintech; innovation; decentralization; blockchain programming; blockchain applications; solidity; cryptography

CONTENTS

LIST OF FIGURES

LIST OF TABLES

PRAISE FOR FUNDAMENTALS OF SMART CONTRACT SECURITY

"I hope that Fundamentals of Smart Contract Security will draw more cybersecurity minded individuals to work in the blockchain space and enable developers to think more actively about programming defensively enabling them to stay on top of security best practices."

—Joseph Lubin, Founder of ConsenSys, Co-founder of Ethereum

"Now you don't have to be a researcher at MIT or a professional security auditor to understand how to build smart contracts, as their new book on Fundamentals of Smart Contract Security explains precisely how to secure smart contracts yourself! Also, as an added benefit, cutting-edge techniques such as symbolic execution are also given an excellent treatment."

—Harry Halpin, blockchain researcher at MIT and Inria de Paris

"In the wake of the BatchOverflow and ProxyOverlow bugs, a highly qualified Quantstamp worked fast and efficiently to help ensure ERC token contracts on our exchange were secure. We were impressed with their knowledge of the latest smart contract vulnerabilities, and their expertise in automated and manual auditing processes."

—Ted Lin, Chief Growth Officer, Binance

"The blockchain space is all about democratization. Up to now, auditing smart contracts to ensure their secure functioning has required arcane knowledge beyond the reach of all but the most experienced blockchain developers. The field is now open to any developer willing to put in the time and effort to read this book and practice its methods. For this reason, it's game-changing and an immensely valuable addition to the body of shared knowledge."

—Lane Rettig, Ethereum Core Developer

"Smart contracts and programmable money enable a wealth of new possibilities, but their immutable and public nature means security must be given top priority. This book will teach you how."
—Eric Ly, Co-founder, LinkedIn, and CEO of Hub Token

"The promise of blockchain won't be realized unless it can be used safely. This book shares insights from the team that knows best how to make that happen."
—Seth Bannon, Founding Partner of Fifty Years

"A timely and impressive resource written by a team that has been on top of smart contracts for years. They give us confidence about the future of smart contracts."
—Mick Hagen, Founder & CEO of Mainframe

"A valuable guide for anyone who is serious about smart contracts and their security. Quantstamp worked hand in hand with our smart contracts engineers and creators to ensure our smart contracts are were secure and our code quality was high."
—Omri Ross, Chief Blockchain Scientist, eToro

"Quantstamp has secured many high-value smart contracts and the expertise captured in this book is an important resource for all smart contracts developers."
—Noah Thorp, Vice President of Engineering, Sharespost

"If you're serious about security, follow the guidance in this book. Quantstamp has audited large-scale, mission-critical initiatives and their expertise in smart contracts security is unparalleled."
—Vansa Chatikavanij, CEO of OmiseGO

FOREWORD

Since going overseas as a soccer player in 2008, I had the opportunity to visit more than 50 countries. This experience made me realize that Japan, the country I grew up in, was wonderful. However, there are countries that do not allow freedom of expression and choice. Places where children are unable to pursue their dreams due to economic or social hardships. I wanted to find a way to change this...to try and help solve these problems.

As a direct approach, I started my soccer school in 2012. As an indirect solution, we started investing in startups in 2016. I hope that supporting wonderful entrepreneurs worldwide will help to solve world economic disparity now more than ever.

Around that time, I met Richard Ma and realized we shared a common empathy towards solving these problems. I felt that he was putting together a wonderful team, with members that also shared a passion to improve the world. Richard Ma and his team aim to facilitate the adoption of blockchain technology by enhancing smart contract security.

A smart contract is the decentralization of an agreement or promise where it is impossible to renege or change the agreed-upon outcome once the contract has been deployed. As this technology continues to mature, ultimately all agreements, such as contracts and certificates, will be digitized.

In the future, smart contracts that are transparent and stored in a distributed manner will be a technology that protects the rights of those contract holders from unwanted attempts to break those rights or agreements. In the not too distant future, I believe that those protected promises and rights will positively impact the lives of many people, bringing greater peace and prosperity throughout the world.

I believe Richard and Quantstamp to be a driving force to effect change and I am committed to supporting their continued efforts. This book is an important step forward in the growth of smart contracts and laying the groundwork for a better future.

Keisuke Honda
Co-Founder, Dreamers Fund and Japanese National Team 2008–2018

PREFACE

Security is not a sexy subject—people take the security of their institutions for granted. As Douglas Adams, author of Hitchhiker's Guide to the Galaxy once humorously said, "It's somebody else's problem." Somebody is taking care of it. The brain just edits it out.

And yet, sometimes "somebody else's problem" becomes your problem. I remember the helpless feeling I felt on one warm summer day in June of 2016, when I watched my 1500 ether, the equivalent of $21,000 at the time, disappear. This later became known as "the DAO Attack" and it has completely changed my life.

I remember the eerie feeling of loss. I remember watching in disbelief. I remember the sick feeling in the pit of my stomach and asking myself, "How do I make sure I am never in this situation again?"

It was more than the loss of money. It was about feeling the disappointment of being violated and not being able to stop the perpetrator, seek justice, or make sure that it never happens again to me or others. Isn't the blockchain supposed to be secure?

It was 2016 and I had a front row seat to watch my money stolen, right in front of my eyes. I saw the action unfold on Twitter, as white hat hackers desperately tried to follow the attacker. To this day, the DAO hacker has not been caught.

Then came an even greater disappointment when I understood the full ramifications of the DAO Hack, which led to the Ethereum fork on July 20, 2016. I thought: "This is a huge setback. If this leads to people giving up on this technology we'll have lost years of progress."

We later learned the DAO Attack was a simple exploit. The DAO project was hacked on or about June 18th, 2016. The attacker drained more than 3.6m ether into a separate contract. The amount stolen was more than $50M at the time of the attack. Smart contracts hold millions of dollars of assets and are high-value targets.

Fast forward to July 2017—Steven Stewart and I co-founded Quant-stamp, a company with a simple yet powerful mission: secure smart contracts to help normal people use them safely and proliferate this amazing technology to solve problems that haven't been solved before.

"The blockchain is secure, smart contracts are not," later became our go-to-line when we witnessed other hacks that have led to losses and disappointments. There was Parity's multi-signature wallet hack, which cost $30M. And then there was the user-triggered wallet freeze, which cost around $280M.

Our understanding of exploits is maturing as technology develops and new types of exploits are discovered. In a recent study done by the National University of Singapore, over 34,000 smart contracts were found to be potentially vulnerable to hacks.

At the same time, smart contracts are also rapidly gaining adoption. In the last 18 months alone, over $11 billion dollars has been raised via smart contracts. From only 500,000 smart contracts in existence a year ago to over 8,000,000 today, interest in smart contracts has grown exponentially. These systems are incredibly powerful, enabling large-scale economic systems to operate without any need for human intervention.

We believe programmable money is a key innovation, solving the problem of trust in an increasingly digital world. That is why we have written this book—our goal is to help the first billion people use blockchain in a safe and secure manner, and to truly make security "somebody else's problem."

Richard Ma
Co-founder and CEO, Quantstamp, Inc.
October 30, 2018

ACKNOWLEDGMENTS

This book was a collective effort of many who are dedicated to the furthering of knowledge in the field of smart contracts. Many talented people with a shared mission helped us along the way, cheerleading us, and giving an incredible amount of time to make it a reality.

From the very beginning, putting this book together was a team effort. I could not have done it without the help of Jan Gorzny, Edward Zulkoski, Kacper Bak, Olga V. Mack, my co-authors, who have given me more ideas and inspiration than I could have ever imagined. They were instrumental in diving deep and pushing the book forward.

Alex Murashkin, Dr. Martin Derka, Nadir Akhtar, Dr. Leonardo Passos, and Dr. Vajih Montaghami also contributed significantly to this book. It required massive amounts of research in a fast-changing world of technology. It is a pleasure to be surrounded by such talented people.

Dan Zhang, Julian Martinez, and Karina Crooks were the dedicated editors of every word on every page. After numerous iterations, they provided much-needed feedback to complete this book. You were instrumental in polishing our prose and structuring our arguments.

Blake Moorhouse helped with the illustrations.

We'd like to thank our academic collaborators, Prof. Vijay Ganesh, Prof. Harry Halpin, Prof. Prateek Saxena, Prof. Martin Vechev, Dr. Petar Tsankov, Dr. Hubert Ritzdorf, Matthias Egli, and Bernhard Mueller.

A big hug for Steven Stewart, my loyal and wise co-founder, who is always honest and kind with his feedback. He is a cherished collaborator and friend, whose thoughtful input is invaluable. Thank you for doing an amazing job managing the technology team, which made this book possible.

Our sincerest gratitude to the whole Quantstamp family, investors, advisors, professors and friends in every corner of the world, who always supported our mission to protect the new programmable money for millions of people. Thank you for being there. A very special thank you to the Quantstamp community who we serve and who in turn inspire us with witty banter and ideas every day.

Mary, my wife who makes the world go round, and my co-author's families, who supported all of us throughout this journey. They always believe in us before we learned to believe in ourselves. We truly appreciate each and every one of you. Thank you for taking this journey with us. Your understanding and support is critical as we keep completing one adventure after another. For that and so much more, my deepest gratitude and love, now and always.

CHAPTER 1

INTRODUCTION

1.1 WHAT ARE SMART CONTRACTS?

The world is built on trust. From the chips in your phone to the bills and cards in your wallet, everything came together as a result of people and organizations trusting each other.

Consider what we put trust into on a regular basis. We believe in the value of a dollar bill, trusting others to accept pieces of paper in exchange for valuable items like food and electronics. We make agreements with peers, companies, and others on a daily basis, trusting all the parties involved to uphold their responsibilities. We trust institutions such as governments and legal firms to ensure wrongdoers suffer appropriate consequences. We read textbooks on every topic imaginable, trusting in the intelligence of the authors and accepting their word as truth. Every agreement comes together as a result of trust.

But what exactly powers these agreements, and how do we establish trust? Traditionally, legal contracts are the medium through which agreements are expressed and confirmed. In a common language, two parties agree to a set of terms, trusting that a third party will step in to justly mediate disputes and enforce the terms of the contract if the terms of the agreement have been violated [1].

Legal contracts, however, are open to interpretation. Human languages, though aiming for precision, rarely mean precisely the same thing to two different people regardless of the similarities in their knowledge base. Therefore, documents written in human languages require concomitant human interpretation and intervention as a result. This is not only expensive (consider the length of some legal cases) but also opens the possibility that a biased third party may interfere with objective decision making. Is there a way to establish agreements that not only lead to consistent behavior amongst non-trusting parties but that also do not need a third party to enforce every contract?

This is where smart contracts come in. Smart contracts capture the concept of formally describing agreements in a mathematical language. As opposed to traditional legal contracts, smart contracts are written in code, and interpreted and executed by machines. By using a computer language instead of a human language to write smart contracts, the behavior of the contract is now predictable. Unlike a human language, computer languages are not open to interpretation; anything expressed within a computer language will be interpreted the same way by any correctly behaving computer. Hence, smart contracts provide not only unchanging methods to express legal ideas and commitments but also remove human expense and error from the equation. Additionally, institutional organizations are no longer required to mediate situations. Instead, with any trusted computer, the contract's terms can be interpreted and executed all in one.

However, there is one problem; legal contracts rely on third parties for interpretation and enforcement. When it comes to smart contracts, who or what is responsible for determining the final truth? Sure, it must be a computer, but whose? Yours? Mine? The government's? A company's? Whatever computer is trusted with the task of running a smart contract must not be subject to manipulation by any other party with skin in the game either. If they are, then the whole point of a smart contract is defeated, since the terms of the agreement can be violated by a fraudulent third party. Unless a trusted third party exists to enforce all these computations, smart contracts lose their assumed reliability [2, 3].

It wasn't until the advent of blockchain technology that smart contracts became feasible at a large scale. With blockchains, computation can be performed between untrusting peers without the risk of interference, as all computations within a public blockchain network such as Bitcoin and Ethereum are performed by thousands of different entities. These entities can trust that the messages they are sharing between each other are legitimate because each entity verifies that the messages they receive follow the strict rules of the peer to peer network. Hence, any two people who want to set up a smart contract can use the blockchain as the trusted third party, since manipulating blockchain networks requires claiming control of a majority of the voting power in the network, a difficult task to do.

Now, by integrating smart contracts into blockchains, we've achieved a way to make formal agreements accessible to anyone. However, there is one last caveat to tackle: what happens if there's a bug in our code? After all, the purpose of smart contracts is to remove the need for human intervention. However, in the presence of a bug, we hit a troublesome roadblock. A question arises: is the bug analogous to a loophole in a legal contract, undesirable but allowed? Or does this bug need to be resolved, by, say, another authority? If avoiding human intervention, then the answer must be that the bugs are respected as part of the agreement, and that the responsibility for due diligence lies on the authors of the contract and participants in the agreement rather than on refuting the terms of the agreement after the fact. This all boils down to a single question, and the purpose of this book: how do we ensure these agreements are written correctly?

Smart contract security exists precisely to ensure that smart contracts are written in a way that matches expectations, through what are known as smart contract audits. A smart contract audit is a thorough inspection of an individual smart contract or smart contract project to help ensure that the code cannot misbehave in any way or be misused by an attacker. This means not only looking for common computer science vulnerabilities such as integer overflow and memory mismanagement, but also more involved vulnerabilities often encountered in systems programming, such as race conditions. In addition to software vulnerabilities, smart contract audits must also investigate game theoretical security, avoiding misalignment of incentives which could allow an actor to gain an unfair economic advantage even though they're technically following contract logic.

Through smart contract security, it is possible to secure agreements for all kinds of industries and groups around the world, as described further in the following sections.

A smart contract is an application of blockchain technology. It is software that codifies business logic and mimics the logic of a business agreement. Smart contracts do three things:

1. They store rules and agreements made by several parties;
2. They automatically detect when certain conditions have been met; and
3. They self-execute an agreement based on conditions they automatically detect.

Because smart contracts are decentralized and running on blockchains, they minimize the need for intermediaries such as banks, brokers, lawyers, courts, escrow agents, and corporations to guarantee execution.

1.2   A BRIEF HISTORY OF SMART CONTRACTS

The concept of smart contracts was first described in 1994 by Nick Szabo, an American cryptographer and programmer, long before blockchain technology came into existence in 2009 [4]. He defined smart contracts as a "set of promises, specified in digital form, including protocols within which the parties perform on these promises." Szabo's idea could not be actualized in 1996 because the necessary technologies, in particular decentralized computation platforms, did not exist.

In 2009, the first cryptocurrency, Bitcoin, was introduced [5]. This marked the first time that decentralized blockchain technology was ever used. Although innovative, the Bitcoin blockchain only allows simple transactions to take place: transferring bitcoins from one party to another. The programming language for the Bitcoin blockchain, Script, intentionally provides a small range of features and is not capable of supporting complex business logic. Script is not Turing-complete, meaning that it is incapable of performing generic kinds of computation such as loops. Nevertheless, Bitcoin provided the foundation for developing smart contracts and the technology necessary to secure them.

In 2013, Ethereum's blockchain provided the first platform that made it possible to use smart contracts at scale. Vitalik Buterin, the founder of Ethereum, proposed including something akin to a Turing-complete scripting language within the Bitcoin blockchain. By embedding a quasi-Turing-complete language (see Section 2.2.1.1) into a blockchain protocol, many kinds of generic computation can be performed in a decentralized manner. Ethereum now provides the foundation for numerous smart contract applications and currently hosts over one million contracts [6].

1.3 USES OF SMART CONTRACTS

Every smart contract involves two or more parties, independently executing transactions according to observable conditions. With smart contracts, people can easily exchange digital assets such as money, real estate, goods, securities, and other assets. Once the contract is made, it is stored and replicated in a decentralized ledger where information cannot be altered or deleted. Using smart contracts for some use case requires justifying the benefits of a smart contract over the costs, as outlined in the following.

1.3.1 ADVANTAGES OF SMART CONTRACTS

Smart contracts have numerous advantages [7] including:

- **Speed**: Legal documents take months, if not years, to interpret and enforce. The time necessary to interpret and enforce a smart contract is only the time it takes to mine a single block. This saves valuable time compared to traditional legal contracts.

- **Independence**: Third parties are unable to interfere with the operation of secure smart contracts. The program itself enforces contract agreements without requiring a trusted middleman to enforce these agreements.
- **Reliability**: Both the contents of the contract and its execution are more reliable than traditional contracts. Data stored in the blockchain is extremely unlikely to be altered or destroyed. If one party in the contract fails to complete its obligation, the conditions of the smart contract will protect the others. Additionally, a party cannot deny having taken some action, since all decisions and outcomes are saved within the blockchain.
- **No errors**: Automatic transaction execution eliminates human error, ensuring no chance for modification to the contract's end result.
- **Savings**: Smart contracts eliminate expenses for middlemen and reduces operational costs. However, savings are limited to specific kinds of operations. While establishing global ownership of an asset is convenient, even simple operations such as addition are millions of times more expensive on the blockchain compared to centralized systems.

1.3.2 DISADVANTAGES OF SMART CONTRACTS

Though smart contracts have promising potential, they also have their disadvantages [8]:

- **Lack of regulation**: Legal frameworks around blockchain, smart contracts, and cryptocurrencies are still evolving.
- **No central governing body**: Because smart contracts are immutable and self-governing, in most situations, bugs cannot be fixed and transactions cannot be reversed [18].
- **Difficulty in implementation**: Integrating elements of the real world into smart contracts may be costly in terms of time, money, and effort.
- **Difficulty of changing a smart contract**: The immutability of smart contracts is a double-edged sword. If new factors arise, parties cannot easily change the underlying smart contract. Therefore options for supplementary agreements should be considered when using smart contracts.

1.4   WHERE CAN SMART CONTRACTS BE USED?

Smart contracts have the potential to be used in many fields [9]. Industries with administrative and legal overhead, such as finance, e-commerce, insurance, auditing, taxation, and supply chain are an obvious fit. Besides these obvious use cases, there are many other applications waiting to be discovered in the future.

Four uses are detailed in the following text: programmable money (tokens), fundraising or initial coin offerings (ICOs), decentralized organizations (DAOs), and ownable virtual assets.

1.4.1   PROGRAMMABLE MONEY

Using smart contracts to program money is a simple use case of smart contracts. This is where conditions are attached to the transfer of money between various parties. Programmable money generally refers to money, often in the form of cryptocurrency or tokens, that only transfers after pre-determined conditions are met [11].

1.4.1.1   The ERC20 Standard

The most common asset used in smart contracts today are tokens based on the Ethereum ERC20 token standard [10]. The ERC20 token standard is a standard interface for tokens on the Ethereum blockchain. This interface describes the functions and events that an ERC20 token contract has to implement.

The ERC20 standard has enabled the growth of the smart contract industry by standardizing the basic functions and characteristics of tokens used in smart contracts. The standard allows infrastructure such as wallets, exchanges, and block explorers to easily support new ERC20 tokens without having to make significant changes to their codebase.

It should be noted that conforming to the ERC20 token standard facilitates smart contract auditing, but does not guarantee the absence of vulnerabilities.

1.4.2   PROPERTIES OF PROGRAMMABLE MONEY

Smart contracts enable constraints to be programmed into the features of a payment. These constraints include restricting: the time period in which an individual is allowed to make a payment, the minimum or maximum amount someone can send, who can make a payment, and who is allowed to receive a payment.

1.4.2.1 Constraints Can Be Based on Non-payment Data

Besides blockchain-native data, constraints can be added to smart contracts that depend on data from the real world to execute agreements. Oracle services, which are services that make real-world data available on the blockchain, are currently offered by trusted third parties. Examples of information that can be injected into the blockchain by oracle services include stock or commodity prices, weather information, sporting event outcomes, or supply chain events (such as a container arriving at port).

1.4.2.2 Constraints Can Be Added and Removed

Constraints can be added and removed as needed. For instance, someone may only be allowed to make a single transfer to a single person, but the receiver of this transfer is free to transfer their money to anyone.

1.4.2.3 Constraints Can Be Extended

Smart contracts make programmable constraints very flexible by allowing new constraints to be added to existing agreements without losing previously defined constraints. For instance, a person can be allowed to spend money without restrictions for a fixed amount of time. After this time has expired, an additional constraint can be added that only allows a person to transfer money to a limited number of recipients.

1.4.2.4 Atomic Transactions

It is possible to simultaneously exchange digital assets in a single transaction because smart contracts enable atomic transactions. The advantage of atomic transactions is that they reduce counterparty risk because the assets are exchanged simultaneously or not at all.

1.4.2.5 Directly Controlled

Users can send and execute transactions directly to the blockchain without the need for interference of third parties. This is in stark contrast to conventional payment systems that first must send instructions to financial institutions before a payment can be executed. This exposes customers to the risk of having their accounts frozen by financial institutions or the risk of experiencing default on the side of the same financial institutions they rely upon.

1.4.3 WHY PROGRAMMABLE MONEY

Selected examples of how programmable money can be used are given below. These examples are not exhaustive and they are only used demonstrates how the properties of programmable money can be applied in practice.

1.4.3.1 Crowdfunding

A condition can be programmed into crowdsales that allow for refunds to automatically take place if the crowdsale fails to raise a predetermined amount of money within a predetermined time period. Also, conditions can be placed on how fast the funds raised can be spent and who is allowed to spend it.

1.4.3.2 Escrow

Programmable money can be used to hold funds in a trust controlled by a third party. A condition can be placed on the trust that requires M of N signatures from multiple parties before escrowed funds can be released to a beneficiary. These conditions can be applied to money held in trust until a child attains a particular age or collateral for a financial transaction.

1.4.3.3 Auctions

To minimize the risk of default in auctions, bidders can be required to send money into an escrow account. If a user wins the auction, their funds can be programmed to instantly transfer to the seller. Additionally, all non-winning bids can be refunded once the auction ends.

1.4.3.4 Charity Donations

Charity donations can have conditions placed on them that restrict when funds can be transferred and to whom it can be sent. Restrictions on who can receive payments can also be pre-approved or authorized through data oracles. Other examples of use cases that restrict how money can be spent include grants, welfare payments, and political donations.

1.4.3.5 Know Your Client (KYC)/Anti-Money Laundering (AML)

Constraints can also limit who is eligible to receive payments. For instance, we can restrict recipients of token transfers to individuals who are already verified via a KYC and AML processes.

1.4.3.6 Loyalty Points

Programmable money can be used by organizations to put conditions on money credited to their customers as a reward for patronage.

1.4.3.7 Direct Debits

Money can be programmed to authorize a company to periodically transfer money out of a customer's account. The time window, amount and/ or number of times a transfer can take place can also be specified. These conditions can be used in the context of a retail customer who authorizes a utility company to debit them on a periodic basis.

1.4.4 FUNDRAISING (ICOS)

In the cryptocurrency world, ICOs [12] act as a form of fundraiser for companies attempting to develop a blockchain application or service. Companies conducting an ICO will sell tokens in exchange for fiat money or cryptocurrency. The company uses these newly acquired funds to create a new blockchain application or service. Token purchasers often buy these tokens to utilize them in the application or service that the company is developing.

Smart contracts are an integral component of ICOs. They are usually used to automatically, openly, and transparently keep track of who made a contribution, determine the number of tokens that each contributor will receive upon the completion of the token sale, decide when contributors should receive a refund, distribute newly minted ICO tokens, and carry out other critical functions in the ICO process.

Before conducting an ICO, companies must prioritize writing high-quality ICO smart contracts. In 2017, ICO smart contracts frequently handled millions of dollars worth of cryptocurrency contributions. Errors in these smart contracts can have devastating financial consequences to both the fundraising company and their contributors, and can jeopardize the reputation of groups involved in the project.

In order to facilitate a successful ICO, it is important to allocate three to six months to create and test ICO smart contracts. Acquiring an audit from at least one third-party is also an essential best practice. Auditing companies are experienced in finding common vulnerabilities, can increase the likelihood that contracts behave as expected, and can increase the likelihood of a successful ICO [13].

1.4.5 DECENTRALIZED AUTONOMOUS ORGANIZATIONS (DAOS)

Traditionally, only a small group of individuals make decisions in a company or organization. In a DAO[14], rules and regulations are enforced by a series of smart contracts that govern the direction and progress of an organization. The goal of a DAO is to eliminate human error, biases and corruption, and increase the efficiency of decision making. A DAO is often regarded as the most complex use case of smart contracts.

1.4.5.1 Disrupting Governance with DAOs

DAOs have the potential to disrupt many traditional governance structures. Large parts of our society are traditionally organized in a hierarchy, but DAOs hope to provide a more decentralized and spontaneous coordination rather than rigid structures. This new form of coordination aims to solve two major problems of traditional governance structures: (1) the principal-agent dilemma, and (2) high transaction costs of coordination.

The principal-agent problem occurs when an agent, a person or entity, can make decisions on behalf of, or impacting, a so-called principal, another person or entity. This situation creates the risk for moral hazard. Moral hazard occurs when one person is willing to take on more risk because someone else bears the cost of those risks. DAOs aim to remove the need for a principle-agent through the use of smart contracts.

DAOs may also reduce problems associated with coordination and levels of bureaucracy. By having rules publicly known to participants and enforcing these rules with smart contracts, it is suspected that DAOs might make coordinating decisions more efficient.

1.4.5.2 How DAOs Work

DAOs operate by rules encoded in smart contracts. A DAO is an entity that exists autonomously on the Internet, but it also heavily relies on individuals to perform certain tasks that the automaton itself cannot do.

Tokens: for a DAO to exist, it needs an internal asset like a token, and it can use that asset as a mechanism to reward certain activities. Once a DAO is created, participants usually fund DAOs with ether in exchange for tokens unique to the DAO.

Transparency: once deployed, the ideal DAO is independent of its creator and external forces cannot influence it. In order for DAO participants to trust that a DAO is truly free from external influence, it relies on transparency. DAOs operate on open source software and publicly available smart contracts, and DAO financial transactions are publicly viewable on the blockchain.

Consensus: to transfer or withdraw funds from a DAO, its stakeholders must agree on a decision through a vote. Even if a bug is found in the DAO's smart contract, this bug cannot be fixed until a majority of voters agree that a bug exists. Although democratic, this process can leave known security vulnerabilities open to exploitation for a period of time.

Contractors: a DAO cannot build a product, write code, or develop hardware; it requires a human to carry its goals and decisions. Contractors can be appointed through the voting of DAO token holders.

Proposals: decisions are made by voting on proposals. In order to prevent people from spamming the network with weak or malicious proposals, proposers are often required to submit a deposit.

Voting: voting takes place after a proposal is submitted. After a proposal is accepted, DAOs can offer people the opportunity to exchange economic value with anyone in the world. In theory, a DAO can execute projects, fundraise, and lend money without requiring an intermediary.

1.4.6 OWNABLE VIRTUAL ASSETS (FOR EXAMPLE, CRYPTOKITTIES/NON-FUNGIBLE ASSETS)

Ether, the cryptocurrency on the Ethereum network, is fungible. If you gave me 1 ether and I now have a total of 2 ether in my wallet, there is no easy way for me to tell which ether came from you. This is because each ether is identical, interchangeable, and indistinguishable from any other.

In order to enable the ownership of virtual assets, non-fungible tokens (NFTs) were created. NFTs allow users to track the ownership of digital assets that have unique identities and attributes. The most popular example of ownable virtual assets is CryptoKitties [15, 47].

CryptoKitties is a virtual game enabled by smart contracts and developed by Axiom Zen. The game allows players to purchase, collect, breed, and sell different types of virtual cats. CryptoKitties is one of the earliest attempts to deploy blockchain technology for the purpose of recreation and leisure. In December 2017, the game was so successful that it led to the congestion of the Ethereum network.

CryptoKitties is not a cryptocurrency. It rather operates on Ethereum's underlying blockchain network as an NFT unique to each CryptoKitty. Every CryptoKitty is unique, owned by the user, validated through the blockchain, and its value can appreciate or depreciate based on the will of the market. CryptoKitties can neither be replicated nor transferred even by the game developers without the user's permission.

Although CryptoKitties is the most popular example of a NFT, the NFT standard can be used to also track ownership of property, other digital collectibles, and land in virtual reality. More NFT use cases are expected to emerge in the future.

1.4.6.1 Technology Behind CryptoKitties

CryptoKitty ownership is tracked through a smart contract on the Ethereum blockchain. They are distributed automatically through a smart contract at the rate of one every 15 minutes (that is 672 per week) for one year. Each CryptoKitty is represented as a non-fungible ERC-721 token [16], allowing each entity to have unique "cattributes."

There is a limit of four billion total cats that can be bred. However, this depends on the limited number of cats going into circulation and their limited genomes. Each cat will have a distinct visual appearance ("phenotype") determined by its immutable genes ("genotype") stored in the smart contract. Since cats are tokens on a blockchain, you can buy, sell, or transfer them digitally, with strong guarantees of ownership. CryptoKitties have no permanently assigned gender. While they can only engage in one breeding session at one time, each cat can act as either a matron or sire. The owner chooses for each breeding interaction.

Axiom Zen Innovation Studio intends to continually release a new CrytoKitty every 15 minutes until November 2018. The rest of the supply will be determined by breeding CryptoKitties. Owners can sell their CrytoKitties via an auction for a price set in ether.

1.4.7 DECENTRALIZED APPLICATIONS (DAPPS)

Decentralized applications (dApps) refers to applications that run on a peer-to-peer (P2P) network of computers instead of a single computer [17]. These types of applications have been in existence since the introduction of P2P networks and cannot be controlled by a single entity.

dApps don't necessarily need to run on a blockchain network. For example, Popcorn Time, BitTorrent, BitMessage, and Tor are all conventional dApps that run on a P2P network but not a blockchain.

1.4.7.1 Difference Between dApps and Smart Contracts

The difference between a dApp and a smart contract is that a dApp is composed of both a front-end and back-end of a blockchain based application, while a smart contract only enables the blockchain based back-end of a dApp. A simple way to understand this difference is to know how conventional websites operate.

The traditional web application uses HTML, CSS, and Javascript to render a page. It will also need to grab details from a database utilizing an API. For example, when you log onto Facebook, the page will call an API to grab your personal data and display it on the page.

dApps are similar to a conventional web application. The front end uses the same technology to render the page. The major difference is that rather than an API connecting to a traditional database, a dApp connects to smart contracts that govern the back-end logic and the database you are connecting to is the blockchain itself.

As you can see, a smart contract is only a small part of an entire dApp. If you want to create a decentralized application on a smart contract platform, you may need to utilize more than one smart contract and may depend on third-party systems for operating the front-end.

Smart contracts are executed the way they are programmed without any deviation and ensure no downtime, no censorship, no fraud and no third party intervention.

1.5 MAJOR HACKS

While proof-of-work blockchains are very secure and have a small attack surface, the same cannot be said of smart contracts. In recent times, security vulnerabilities found in smart contracts have led to users losing over $230 million dollars worth of cryptocurrency. In this section, we will review prominent smart contract hacks including the DAO hack, the Parity multisig wallet hacks, and the BatchOverflow hacks and discuss their impact on the smart contract ecosystem.

1.5.1 DAO HACK

In 2016, the Decentralized Autonomous Organization (The DAO) was created to operate like a venture capital fund for cryptocurrency projects. It was built using several smart contracts published on the Ethereum blockchain. The DAO was very popular, raising over $150 million from more than 11,000 members, making it the largest crowdfunding event ever at the time.

There was tremendous enthusiasm for the DAO within the Ethereum community at the time because the DAO was simultaneously a proof of concept for a new smart contract use case, and many believed this organization would fund projects that would further advance the Ethereum ecosystem. Despite early enthusiasm, some members of the Ethereum community called for a moratorium on the project due to suspected security vulnerabilities.

1.5.1.1 The Hack

In June 2016, a hacker stole about 3.6 million ether from the DAO smart contract within a few hours. This ether was worth approximately $50 million at the time. The hacker was able to get the DAO smart contract to return ether multiple times before it could update its own balance. Two main flaws can be traced to this hack. First, the smart contract transferred ether to the hacker before updating its internal token balance. Second, the DAO coders failed to take into consideration the possibility of a recursive call that could act in this way [18]. For a detailed look at the mechanism of the DAO hack, see section 4.4—Re-entrancy.

1.5.1.2 The Hard Fork

The consequences of the DAO hack had lasting political implications for the Ethereum community. In order to refund the lost ether to DAO participants, the Ethereum community decided to create a hard fork which essentially removed the hack from the history of the blockchain. Although the hard fork successfully undid the hack, the hard fork was extremely controversial because it did not respect the immutability of the Ethereum blockchain.

1.5.2 PARITY WALLET HACKS

Multisignature wallets are smart contracts designed to manage crypto assets with consent by multiple wallet owners. These wallets usually allow owners to set daily withdrawal limits, vote for withdrawals, and ownership changes, and can include other features as well.

In July 2017, a hacker was able to steal over 150,000 ether, worth approximately $30 million US dollars at the time, from popular multisignature wallets developed by Parity Technologies [19].

The hacker was able to steal these funds by taking advantage of a bug that allowed the hacker to claim ownership of three multisignature wallets. The hacks each took place in only two transactions for each wallet: one to claim sole ownership of the wallet, and the other to remove all funds.

Parity Technologies issued an update to attempt to resolve this issue, but on November 2017, only 3 months later, another vulnerability led to 513,744.16 ether worth over $150 million US dollars to be permanently frozen [20]. Several companies that conducted high profile ICOs were affected by this vulnerability.

1.5.3 BATCHOVERFLOW

ERC20 tokens conform to a common interface defining basic rules of ownership and coin transfer [49]. Most of the coins reuse certified smart contract templates to avoid the risk of introducing a new bug to an already-proven formula [21].

Some ICO companies decided to include additional functionalities to these templates. One of these additional functionalities is what introduced the BatchOverflow bug to several ERC20 tokens. The hackers were able to take advantage of this bug by giving themselves extremely large quantities of the affected token. When the BatchOverflow vulnerability was discovered, several crypto exchanges halted trading, deposits and withdrawals of all ERC20 tokens until they could determine which tokens were affected.

1.6 THE NEED FOR SECURE SMART CONTRACTS

Smart contracts have enabled exciting new use cases and unforeseen use cases will likely emerge in the future. During the early stages of development of the Internet, it was difficult to imagine applications like YouTube, Amazon Web Services, and Facebook having such a presence in our everyday lives. Although developers creating the Internet in these early days could not predict the emergence of these applications, they could not help but feel like something big was on the horizon.

The same early optimism that existed in 1994 now exists for smart contract technology; however, in order for smart contract technology to proliferate and achieve its full potential, smart contract security needs to be addressed [22]. Smart contracts will fail to achieve mainstream adoption if a single line of code can lead to millions of dollars worth of digital assets to be lost or stolen.

In the following chapters, we will cover how blockchains function, design choices for smart contract development, common vulnerabilities found in smart contracts, and finally the best practices for writing smart contracts.

The discussions in this book are not exhaustive. This book is meant to highlight key concepts and share pragmatic information. The topics were selected with the intention to provide the reader with practical and real-world relevance. It must also be noted that blockchain and smart contract technology is still evolving and new information regarding smart contract security will continue to emerge. After reading this book it is important to not only be familiar with the Ethereum Whitepaper [23], and Yellowpaper [24] but stay up to date with trends in the field.

CHAPTER 2

THE STATE OF BLOCKCHAIN SECURITY

To understand smart contract security we have to understand the technology underpinning it: the blockchain. This chapter gives a technical overview of blockchain mechanics before talking about the security layers of blockchain. Readers who already possess a solid understanding of blockchain mechanics may want to skip Section 2.1 and go directly to Section 2.2 which focuses on the aspects of blockchain technology most relevant to smart contract security.

2.1 BLOCKCHAIN FUNDAMENTALS

A blockchain is a decentralized, append-only ledger. Similar to a linked-list, a blockchain is a collection of blocks connected through hashes into a chain-like structure. Blocks store transactions changing the state of the blockchain by updating either account funds or the persistent storage of smart contracts.

2.1.1 UTXO VERSUS ACCOUNT-BASED BLOCKCHAINS

Different blockchains represent transactions in different ways. Two common models are unspent transaction outputs (UTXOs) and accounts. Bitcoin relies on UTXOs, whereas Ethereum relies on the account model.

The UTXO model enables parallel transactions, as multiple UTXOs can be processed at the same time, and easy privacy (or obfuscation) provided a user sends a UTXO to a new address every time. The account model is simpler to understand and implement, and also provides more efficient transaction validation by removing the need to find the addresses of all consumed UTXOs.

These models are not mutually exclusive. For instance, Plasma, a design pattern for scaling Ethereum-based applications, may use the notion of UTXOs on top of the account-based model of Ethereum [45, 46].

2.1.1.1 The UTXO Model

UTXOs denote outputs of a transaction that have not been spent. In blockchains using UTXOs, each transaction spends previously created UTXOs while potentially creating new ones. Each UTXO has an associated value. Any given transaction is valid if it has a valid signature (this is to prevent forging) and none of the UTXOs it consumes has been previously spent. In the UTXO model, users do not have accounts; instead, they own the private key to each address that contains a UTXO they own.

Figure 2.1 shows a sequence of transactions illustrating these concepts. Transaction 1 creates outputs (2) and (4), which are spent by transactions 2 and 3, respectively—these are consumed and are not UTXOs. No transaction consumes the outputs of transaction 3; thus, they are all UTXOs.

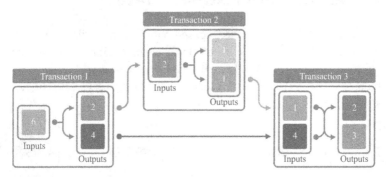

Figure 2.1. Transactions in the UTXO model.

2.1.1.2 The Account-Based Model

In contrast with UTXOs, used by Bitcoin, the account-based model, used by Ethereum, is a bit more sophisticated. In Ethereum, an account address is a fixed-sized string of 160 bits—40 hexadecimal characters.

Ethereum accounts have:

1. An Ether balance (possibly empty);
2. A *transaction nonce*[1] denoting the number of transactions sent from the account;
3. A mapping of 256-bit words to other 256-bit words, representing the account's persistent storage;
4. The compiled code (bytecode) of a given contract. Associating code to an address only applies to smart contract accounts.

An Ethereum account that is not associated with a smart contract is called an *externally owned account* (EOA). Sending transactions from an EOA requires signing them to prevent identity forging. Signatures work as follows. An EOA holder has a public-private key pair. The public key of an EOA is the address. After signing a transaction with the private key, the signed transaction can only be verified by the corresponding public key (address). Thus, a recipient of a signed transaction is assured of its origin. An address' private key should never be shared; the public key is freely available to all participants of the blockchain.

Transactions operate differently depending on the nature of the target account. Sending a transaction to a smart contract account calls for a function execution (by default, the fallback function). Sending a transaction to an EOA transfers some amount (possibly zero) of Ether to that address.

The bytecode associated with an address is the compiled version of a smart contract written in a high-level language (e.g., Solidity).

To allow other accounts to interact with a contract, developers must deploy the compiled contract to a unique address. In Ethereum, developers cannot choose such addresses; rather they are generated automatically. Once deployed, smart contracts are immutable: their bytecode cannot be changed.

2.1.2 CHAINING BLOCKS: LET'S HASH!

2.1.2.1 Blockchain Contents

The blocks within a blockchain are a coarse-grain unit for storing information. A block stores:

1. An ordered collection of transactions
2. A timestamp

---

[1] This differs from the *block nonce*, which we describe later.

3. The hash of the previous block

4. A merkle root

Hashes are output values of *hash functions*, which can be thought of as generating a unique representation from a given input—in this case, the preceding block. This hash links each block with the previous block, forming a blockchain. The only block not storing the hash of its preceding block is the first block, a.k.a. the *genesis block*.

The merkle root is the root of the merkle tree: a binary hash tree of all the transactions in the block. The merkle root helps verify transactions in the block and is explained in-depth later.

On some blockchains, blocks also store an additional value: the *block nonce*: a number certifying that some computation effort has been placed to grant the right to add the current block to the blockchain. Nonces occur in any blockchain using Proof of Work (PoW) consensus, such as Ethereum. We will explain the PoW consensus mechanism later in this chapter.

With the exception of the last block, a block may be a *parent* to other blocks—so-called *child* blocks. Figure 2.2 provides an example: block $n-1$ is the parent of block n. We can also say that block n is a child of block $n-1$.

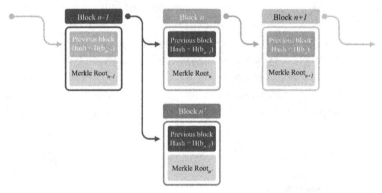

Figure 2.2. A simplified blockchain. Each b_i is a block, where *Merkle Root_i* is the merkle root of transactions included in the block b_i, and $h(b_i)=h(i\|h(b_{i-1})\|Merkle\ Root_{i-1})$ where $x\|b$ indicates the concatenation of strings x and b. Nonces are not included in this diagram.

2.1.2.2 Cryptographic Hashes

Hashes are a core concept in blockchain. This is not a coincidence; hashes have desirable properties that help structure and secure the entire blockchain.

At a minimum, a hash function h has a compressed, fixed-sized output. Independently of the length of x, the output $y=h(x)$ is a small constant size, typically a few hundred bits. Ethereum, for instance, uses the Keccak-256 hash function—given an input of arbitrary length, the output always has 256 bits. In practice, hash functions have two other desirable properties:

H1 *deterministic*: given an input x, $h(x)$ always produce the same value;
H2 *efficient*: computing $h(x)$ given x is quick.

While useful, properties H1 and H2 are not enough to guarantee the structure of the blockchain. The latter requires the use of *cryptographic hash functions*. In comparison to hash functions, cryptographic hash functions have five additional properties, namely:

H3 *uniformity*: the input values to a cryptographic function h map evenly to the possible set of output values;
H4 *apparent randomness*: for any two distinct values x_i and x_j, even when x_i is similar to x_j, the outputs $h(x_i)$ and $h(x_j)$ appear random;
H5 *collision resistant*: it should be difficult to find two inputs x_1 and x_2 such that $x_1 \neq x_2$ and $h(x_1)=h(x_2)$;
H6 *pre-image resistant*: given an output y of the appropriate (such a function is called *one-way*) output size (e.g., given in bits), it should be infeasible to find an input x such that $y=h(x)$;
H7 *second pre-image resistant*: given x_1 it should be infeasible to find x_2 such that $h(x_1)=h(x_2)$.

In the remainder of this chapter, we use the terms hash functions and hashes in reference to cryptographic hash functions and the output values they produce.

Collision resistance and second pre-image resistance are similar, but not equal properties. The former guards against the ability to find any two inputs that are different, but hash to the same value; the latter guards against the ability to find a second value that hashes to the same value of some specific input.

2.1.2.3 Securing the Blockchain

With the understanding of what a cryptographic hash function is, let's revisit the blockchain structure, the connection between blocks, and the security guarantees that arise as a consequence.

As we discussed previously, blocks are connected via hashes. Due to the randomness and collision resistant nature of hashes, connections among blocks are unique. Hence, each block has a single parent. The genesis block is the only exception—as it is the first block, it has no parent. This uniqueness sets the basic foundation to protect against data tampering.

For instance, assume that an attacker wants to tamper with a block b. The block which has been tampered with, say $t(b)$, will have a different hash than b. Since all the child blocks chained to b store its hash, the hashes of each child must be recalculated if they are to be chained to $t(b)$. That, in turn, requires changing the hash of each block chained to each child block of b. This process continues until all blocks coming after b are changed. Since hashes are fairly cheap to compute, the burden of recomputing them is not necessarily prohibitive. Thus, attackers may still be incentivized to tamper with the blockchain.

Blockchains are designed to prevent this kind of data tampering. Ethereum and Bitcoin achieve this by associating a hard to guess number with each block. This number—the block nonce—is itself stored in the block. Hashing is performed not on a target block, but its concatenation with its nonce. Thus, to tamper with a block, an attacker is forced to recompute not just the hashes but also new nonces of each subsequent block. Thus, these blockchains prevent data tampering by ensuring that recomputing block hashes must require attackers to spend an unfeasibly large amount of time and computation power.

2.1.2.4   The Merkle Tree

In both Bitcoin and Ethereum, transaction data is recorded in a block via a *merkle tree*. A merkle tree is a data structure that relies on cryptographic hash function. To put it simply, a merkle tree has a *root* which is a hash of the hashes of some set of data. As a result, changing the data (in this case, a transaction), changes the root. A merkle root is, therefore, a concise signature of the data in a block.

Given a collection of data D, a Merkle Tree is a binary tree that has $|D|$ leaves: one for each datum $d \in D$. Each leaf stores the hash $H(d)$ of the data d it represents, and is extended with a child which includes d in plain-text (i.e., prior to hashing). Every internal node in the tree is the hash $H(c_1, c_2)$ of its (at most two) children, c_1 and c_2. As a result of this construction, changing the value in any one leaf, changes all hashes from the root of the tree to that leaf, including most importantly, the root hash itself. An example of a Merkle tree is shown in Figure 2.3.

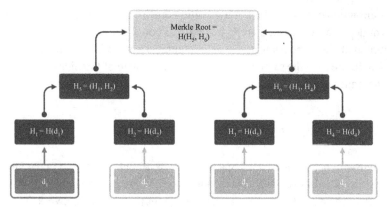

Figure 2.3. A merkle tree storing four data.

Checking if data is present in a Merkle tree is efficient. In order to determine if a leaf contains some value, all that is required is the hash of that value, and the hashes used to compute the hashes from the leaf to the root. As a binary tree with l leaves has $\log_2(l)$ levels, only $\log_2(l)$ hashes are necessary; that is, strictly less than all the stored data when $l > 2$.

2.1.3 TRANSACTIONS AND BLOCK MINING

Blocks primarily aggregate transactions. A transaction is an update to the global state of the blockchain. Such updates can be changing someone's balance or the variables in a smart contract. In the latter case, this is generally performed indirectly by calling specific functions of the target contract.

2.1.3.1 Transaction Validity

When users wish to make a new transaction, they create the transaction, digitally sign it with their private key, and broadcast it to the nodes forming the blockchain network. The network maintains a pool of unconfirmed transactions, which are transactions which have been broadcasted to the network but not yet included in a block. Some nodes, known as *miners*, take transactions from this pool, validate them, and include them in a new block.

A transaction is valid if the sender of the funds currently owns the funds, those funds have not previously been spent, and the signature on the transaction can be verified. A transaction that invokes a smart contract call (or deploys a contract, thereby invoking its constructor—an optional function with the same name as the smart contract) is valid if another execution would produce the same result given the same state of the blockchain that the transaction was executed on.

2.1.3.2 Transaction Fees

Transactions provide the means for users to interface with and update the blockchain. As executing transactions requires some computational effort, they have an implicit cost (e.g., electricity) for nodes in the network. Thus, most blockchains charge *transaction fees*.

A transaction fee is a reward for a miner to verify the validity of the transaction, and an incentive to include a particular transaction over others. Miners have a limit on the number of transactions they may include in a block that follows from the limit of the number of transactions a block may store. Since miners may choose any transactions from the pool of unconfirmed ones, miners often choose those transactions for which the fees are highest. As a result of this incentivization scheme, users can choose to pay higher fees in order to maximize the likelihood of their transaction being chosen for the next block, resulting in quicker transaction processing.

Alternatively, users may wish to pay lower fees to save money, and this may result in an increase in the time for the transaction to be included in a new block. Transaction fees must be paid (and calculated) using the native currency only; for example, Bitcoin or Ether, and in particular, cannot be paid using tokens, such as Bitcoin's colored coins or Ethereum's ERC-20 tokens. Transaction fees are only earned by miners if the blockchain network accepts their proposed block.

For the Ethereum blockchain, transaction fees to execute smart contract functions are given as a function of *gas units* (or *gas*, for short), multiplied by the *gas price*. The latter is given in wei, a sub-unit of ether (10^{18} wei=1 ether). By separating the calculation of transaction fees from the price of the underlying ether, Ethereum attempts to decouple the price of transaction and computations from ether price volatility.

When a smart contract function is called, its associated bytecode is executed. Each bytecode instruction refers to an operation identifier—a.k.a. *opcode*. Each opcode, in turn, has a pre-determined gas cost. Simple operations (e.g., adding two numbers) take a small amount of gas; complicated operations (storing data on the blockchain) require a large amount of gas. There is a fixed limit to the maximum amount of gas that a contract can consume in one transaction. The sender of the transaction sets the gas price, resulting in the same cost-vs-inclusion-time trade-off in transfer transactions. The transaction sender may also impose a stricter limit on the amount of gas to be used. If a smart contract's function execution requires more gas than provided, it terminates as if the execution was never attempted. The cost of running the execution is paid to the miner.

From an economic perspective, transaction fees set an incentive for miners to do their work. Miners who propose a new block that eventually gets accepted by the network get to collect the fees of all the transaction in the proposed block. As miners compete against one another, many new blocks may be proposed, and the network must agree on which one to include. Agreement, in this case, can be achieved by different consensus algorithms most notably, *Proof-of-Work*.

Besides incentivizing miners to validate blocks, transaction fees for computational tasks on Ethereum also prevent infinite loops, discourage Denial of Service (DoS) attacks, and encourage efficient code.

2.1.4 UNDERSTANDING PROOF OF WORK

Proof of Work (PoW) is the consensus mechanism for the Bitcoin blockchain and also the current version of the Ethereum blockchain. It uses rewards to incentivize miners to perform computational tasks that benefit the network.

2.1.4.1 Proof of Work Consensus

Proof of Work (PoW) is a specialization of the *Nakamoto Consensus Algorithm*. In Nakamoto consensus, a leader is elected in order to propose a new block, and other participants implicitly vote on the correctness of the block by appending their blocks to it. PoW elects leaders based on how much computational power nodes contribute to solving a challenge.

PoW is an algorithm designed to ensure consensus among nodes, while providing economic incentives to miners. PoW operates by requiring miners to provide the solution to a fresh computational challenge before submitting a block to the blockchain. The specific challenge depends on the blockchain and PoW setting. The computational challenge must be hard to solve, but easy to verify. Furthermore, the computational challenge should be difficult to solve even in the presence of very specialized hardware; for instance, as with application-specific integrated circuit (ASIC) miners. Ethereum relies on `Ethash`, an ASIC-resistant PoW algorithm.

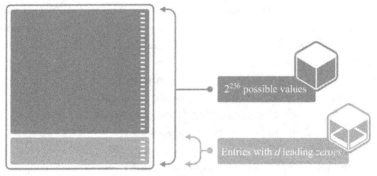

Figure 2.4. There are 2^{256} possible outcomes for a hash function with output size 256-bits, each just as likely as any other (property H3 of cryptographic hash functions). Finding a value n so that $H(n\|b_j)$ starts with a specific number of leading 0s requires guessing values until a hash in the desired range occurs.

In general terms, the idea behind PoW algorithms is to find a *block nonce* that, if concatenated with the data of a proposed block, hashes to a small value below some threshold. Figure 2.4 details this further. Because hashes are random, there is no way to predict what value the nonce should be; the best approach is to try all values. Setting the threshold sufficiently small is already enough to require billions of guesses on average before a suitable nonce is found. Once a node finds a nonce, its value is included in the block, which is then submitted to the blockchain. When that happens, the block is said to be *mined*. In Ethereum, new blocks are mined, on average, every 15 seconds [41].

2.1.4.2 Mining Rewards

In addition to transaction fees, PoW includes additional miner rewards, as guessing billions of hash values is an expensive process. Miners who successfully submit a valid block (with a valid nonce) receive some value of newly minted currency. This reward offsets the cost of operating the hardware for mining blocks. Currently, mining a new Ethereum block awards 2 ether to the miner.

PoW parameters such as miner reward and mining difficulty are not fixed. For instance, typically the reward for mining a new block decreases over time. This decrease accounts for the expected increase of value per unit of currency while preventing the flooding of new coins on the given network. Mining difficulty tends to increase over time. This is meant to offset the increased performance of faster computational hardware coming to market over time.

2.1.4.3 Forks

As mining occurs, multiple miners may propose blocks around the same time. In this case, a *fork* occurs, and the blockchain is split. Hence, miners may have multiple chains to extend when proposing new blocks. In the event of a fork, the longest chain[2] (a.k.a. the *canonical chain*) is chosen to be the one reflecting the current state of the blockchain. That follows from the fact that the longest chain is the one where most computation effort has been put. Every now and then, however, it happens that miners add their blocks to chains that do not end being the longest. These blocks are said to be *orphaned*. Let's look at an example of this.

Back in Figure 2.2, block n' is orphaned; block $n-1 \leftarrow$ block $n \leftarrow$ block $n+1$ is the canonical chain. An orphaned block at the same height as some parent block on the canonical chain is called an *uncle* block. Back to our example, block n' is an uncle block of block $n+1$.

Miner rewards (and earned transaction fees) on the orphaned chain are useless, unless the chain explicitly rewards these blocks.[3] Similarly, transactions in an orphaned block are not final until they are included in blocks on the canonical chain. This is an additional incentive for rational miners to choose the same chain: if they do not, they will not be rewarded.

When multiple chains appear to be the longest, it is unclear which chain will be the canonical chain. Due to this uncertainty, most transactions are not considered final until they are included in a chain to which additional other successive blocks are extended. In Bitcoin, six additional blocks are typically required, while with Ethereum the threshold is usually higher. Although this is just a heuristic, it ensures transactions are in the canonical chain before they are considered final—the likelihood of having these additional blocks appended to an orphaned block is negligible, assuming that the majority of miners are rational.

2.1.4.4 Miner's Dilemma

Current PoW implementations work well most of the time, but they are not perfect. The Miner's Dilemma illustrates one case of misaligned crypto-economic incentives.

Miners are responsible for two conflicting jobs. A miner is responsible for verifying transactions that they include in a block, while also attempting to guess the block's nonce as fast as possible. This results in the

---

[2] In Ethereum, forks which have the largest total difficulty are chosen [54].
[3] Ethereum rewards uncle blocks [53].

so-called *Miner's Dilemma* [44]: the miner wishes to only include valid transactions (as otherwise, they will propose an invalid block which will not be included on the longest chain), while also guessing an appropriate nonce to earn the mining reward. Verifying transactions takes computational resources that could otherwise be utilized to guess nonce values. Therefore, miners may be incentivized in some cases to attempt to skip the validation of blocks with expensive transactions in favor of mining the next block.

2.1.4.5 Proof of Stake

In addition to PoW, other consensus algorithms have been proposed, notably Proof of Stake (PoS). PoS is used in, for example, the PPCoin cryptocurency [48]. In PoS consensus, participants stake some currency on a proposed block being valid. For example, the more currency owned by participants, the more transactions they can validate. In the event that a staked transaction proves to be invalid, the stakers of that transaction lose their stakes. Ethereum is currently planning to transition to PoS. As opposed to PoW, PoS is more efficient as it does not require using brute force calculations to find the solution to a mathematical challenge. PoS does have downsides, however. For instance, if the value of the staked currency is negligible, malicious actors can stake invalid transactions in order to slow down the network. This is the *nothing-at-stake* problem.

2.2 BLOCKCHAIN ENVIRONMENT SECURITY LAYERS

Blockchains have several security layers by design, employing cryptographic primitives and economic models to achieve this security. Smart contracts are secured by the virtual machine, and in some cases, the semantics of the language they are written in (though they also need to be designed and written in a secure manner). Despite these security mechanisms, exploits still exist on all layers: the blockchain mechanics, the virtual machine, and the high-level language for writing smart contracts.

2.2.1 CRYPTOGRAPHY

The first layer of security in any blockchain is its underlying cryptographic hash function. As we discuss in the previous section, hash functions play a vital role connecting blocks, while digital signatures ensure transactions are not forged. A technical introduction to cryptography can be found in, for example, [31].

2.2.1.1 The Hash Function

Ethereum uses the Keccak-256 hash function [28], which hashes inputs to a fixed-length size of 256 bits. Keccak is a family of hashes with varying security properties. It is worth noting that hashes in Ethereum are often referred to as SHA-3 (defined in [29]). This is incorrect.[4] The SHA-3 standard defines a subset of Keccak, with parameters that differ from those in Ethereum. Therefore, hash functions computed on Ethereum may not match the output a given user would expect if SHA-3 were to be used.

The security of hash functions is defined in terms of its resilience to known attacks. The most common measure of hash function security is the size of the output of the hash function, as this determines the time it will take to perform pre-image and collision attacks.

Given a hash function whose outputs are hashes of length n (in bits), it is possible to find pre-images[5] in time 2^n, second pre-images in time 2^n, and collisions in time $\sqrt{2^n} = 2^{n/2}$. If one is to employ a collision attack (i.e., find inputs x, x' such that $h(x')=h(x)$ and $x' \neq x$), the length of the output must be chosen so that even checking the square root of all possible outputs is infeasible. The number $n/2$ is therefore typically called the number of bits of security for a hash function with output size n.

2.2.1.2 Digital Signatures

Ethereum uses the Elliptic Curve Digital Signature Algorithm (ECDSA) [32]. Digital signatures are used to verify the transaction origin and integrity. As mentioned in the previous section, an Ethereum account is a public key to an account. The account owner keeps the corresponding private key a secret. The owner of the private key can sign some message m using their private key, and anyone with access to the corresponding public key can verify that the owner signed m.

A proper digital signature scheme must be able to verify that a transaction's origin comes from the source it claims to be from. This prevents

---

[4] We refer readers to [30]; but readers can also test the differences in outputs.
[5] Given a hash x and a hash function h, a pre-image is a value y where $h(y)=x$.

forging and consequently prevents theft. Assuming a person's private key is not stolen, a digital signature also proves that account sent this transaction.

Transactions themselves must also be secured by the ECDSA. This is achieved by signing the hash $h(t)$ of a given transaction t, which ensures no content is changed. Without this guarantee, a transaction which transfers ether from one account to another could be changed to send an arbitrary amount of ether instead of the intended amount.

2.2.2 VULNERABILITIES

Despite the high level of security provided by the aforementioned cryptographic primitives, the blockchain is not perfect and may be hacked by other means. For instance, as the exact state of a smart contract is hard to predict, timestamps may be modified, and smart contracts relying on randomness may expose a vulnerability to miners, who could be in a position of exploiting the randomization process.

2.2.2.1 The Ethereum Virtual Machine

The Ethereum network can be seen as a decentralized execution environment. Each node in the network executes independently from others; later, nodes reach a consensus on what the state of the blockchain should be. When nodes execute a transaction, they do it in the context of a virtual machine. In Ethereum, this is called the Ethereum Virtual Machine (EVM).

The EVM executes Ethereum bytecode. Bytecode is low-level, machine readable code, but it is not designed for human consumption. Instead, developers rely on high-level languages such as Solidity to write smart contracts, and then use a compiler to translate their contracts into machine-friendly bytecode. Each bytecode instruction refers to an opcode—a numeric identifier for an operation supported by the EVM. Each opcode has a predefined gas cost. Whenever transactions run out of gas, the transaction state is reverted and the gas is consumed.

In theory, if given an infinite amount of gas, EVMs are very powerful. Their opcodes form a *Turing complete* instruction set, that is, they can simulate the execution of any Turing machine (see [27] for more). This is the same as saying the EVM is capable of executing any program that any other computer can. In practice, however, this is not the case—any transaction's execution is limited by an upper gas limit. Consequently, large computations are not feasible; even simple-but-slow algorithms, such as trying every solution to a Sudoku puzzle, proves to be hard because of the large number of computations needed. We therefore say that the EVM is *quasi-Turing Complete*.

When a transaction is executed, the starting state for execution is often unpredictable for the transaction originator. Recall that mined blocks aggregate transactions, with no restriction on how miners order transactions. Thus, a transaction may be placed near the end of a block, wherein it may be preceded by another transaction that affects the state of the contract which the latter transaction is calling. For example, a lottery smart contract may provide an arbitrary account an opportunity to withdraw all funds. An account may wish to make such a withdrawal, but a miner may also wish to include a similar transaction in their block. The miner can order transactions so that theirs is first, thereby winning the race and receiving the funds in the smart contract. One method for mitigating this threat is described in [38].

Moreover, block timestamps can be manipulated when blocks are mined. A miner includes a timestamp for a block, which applies to all transactions within that block. However, if the execution of a smart contract depends on a timestamp of a previous block, the miner may be incentivized to modify the timestamp to gain an advantage.

This is possible because the blockchain has a tolerance for timestamps, to avoid latency issues. The Ethereum blockchain tolerance is described as 15 minutes [24], so rational (or malicious) miners may modify it if they think it will be helpful.

The EVM is deterministic. The state of a smart contract after any block is known, and any miners who create blocks including transactions interacting with that smart contract should provide the same output—unless they are malicious or erroneous. The EVM lacks an opcode for generating random numbers. Therefore, pseudo-randomness is often the only option for contracts relying on non-determinism. Smart contract writers must take care to ensure that contracts behave as expected even in the face of publicly available seeds and number generation functions.

Alternatively, randomness can be generated from future blocks or hidden commitments. Random numbers can be generated by taking information from future blocks, which is hard to predict. However, miners of those future blocks may still benefit from modifying the data in those blocks. A smart contract can obtain random numbers by asking participants to hash a random number and send that hash, along with a deposit. After a set time, the participants are required to submit the number they hashed, or risk losing their deposit; the random number can be used as a function of these submitted values. Attackers could still intentionally sacrifice their deposit if they see that the values submitted by the others (which are transmitted in the clear on the blockchain) combined with their own would result in an unfavorable outcome.

The EVM is well tested, but not necessarily well-documented. The Yellow paper [24] was the first to provide a description of the opcodes in the EVM; others followed by formally describing the semantics of the virtual machine [25, 26, 33, 111]. The latter sources mention that the Yellow Paper contains errors and omissions. Given the complexity of the EVM, this is not surprising. Fortunately, none of these errors resulted in any security risks for smart contract execution.

To further identify potential flaws in the EVM implementation, some researchers set to obtain a *formal model* or *formal specification* of the EVM. Currently, competing models exist. Examples include models written with the K Framework [25, 111] and F* proof assistant [33]. These models enable the checking of properties on the EVM itself, as well as properties of smart contracts executing on the EVM.

The K framework implements an executable EVM environment from a formal specification of the EVM, the expected behavior exhibited by the EVM test suite, and actual EVM behavior. The K framework enables property checking over execution states, and thereby enables a user (in an interactive fashion) to check that properties will hold on their smart contract when it is deployed on the Ethereum blockchain.

The F* proof assistant in [33] relies on a complete semantics of EVM bytecode. The semantics is executable and was validated from the official EVM test suite. The formalization allows the encoding of various security properties and hyper-properties (properties that hold over several contracts), enabling the formal verification of smart contracts executing on top of the EVM.

2.2.3 SOLIDITY AND OTHER LANGUAGES

Solidity [36] is a high-level language designed for writing smart contracts in Ethereum. Solidity is imperative, with a Javascript-like syntax. Its design was influenced by C++, Python, and Javascript. Some automated analysis tools exist for Solidity (e.g., [34, 94]).

2.2.3.1 Solidity Peculiarities

Solidity has some peculiarities that, if not paid attention to, can easily lead to vulnerabilities.

- Every contract attribute can be read by others, even if marked as private. Private attributes cannot be accessed directly, but instead, can be read from the blockchain itself.
- Calling a non-existing function in a contract does not necessarily lead to an error, but will attempt to call the contract's fall-back function—this is known as *call to the unknown.*
- Exception handling is another area of concern; errors do not necessarily propagate across the call-stack—this may depend on certain specifics of the target function (c.g., see .call() vs. .send() vs. .transfer() [55]).
- Types that do not occupy the full 32 bytes on-chain may be stored with arbitrary data ("dirty bits") in the unused fields.
- Inheritance is another major issue with the language. Since Solidity supports multiple inheritance, figuring out what functions get called in the end is difficult. This is particularly worrisome since if the inheritance order is incorrect, one may expose errors in the final contract.[6]

Solidity is not the only language for writing smart contracts. In the following, we briefly discuss other languages compiling to EVM bytecode. There are additional languages in development which are not discussed here (for example, Flint [37]).

2.2.3.2 LLL

Unlike Solidity, *Low-level Lisp-like Language* (LLL) is a functional language for smart contract writing. As its name suggests, LLL is heavily influenced by Lisp—one of the first functional languages proposed in computer science (its origin dates back to the late 50s). Although LLL was one of the first languages that smart contracts could be written in for Ethereum, it did not find widespread adoption amongst developers; in fact, the project is largely abandoned.

2.2.3.3 Serpent

Assembly-like language extended with some high-level constructs. Its use is discouraged for general purpose contract writing. Rather, it should be used when developers need to perform low-level opcode manipulation.

---

[6] See an example at [56].

2.2.3.4 Bamboo

A relatively new smart contract language, Bamboo comes with some interesting features. A contract written in Bamboo declares all states and the transitions amongst them.

Seeing a contract as a state machine is thought to avoid common mistakes in smart contract development. In fact, by design, the language prevents re-entrancy altogether. Re-entrancy is a well-known, yet dangerous vulnerability. It implicitly allows a function to be recursively called many times until a point where the attacker can drain the funds of the target contract—Chapter 4 provides further details. Re-entrancy is at the core of the DAO attack.

2.2.3.5 Vyper

While an experimental language at this stage, Vyper [35] is gaining momentum in the community. The language was designed with security and auditability in mind:

> Vyper code should be maximally human-readable. Furthermore, it should be maximally difficult to write misleading code [43].

As with Bamboo, Vyper is a language trading expressibility and convenience for security. For example, Vyper prohibits loops whose bounds are variable (no recursion is possible, either). This enables easy gas computations, and should increase the effectiveness of formal method tools on these contracts.

A Vyper compiler was formally verified by Runtime Verification Inc. along with the Formal Systems Lab at the University of Illinois (Urbana-Champaign) in the K Framework [39, 40]. The language does not have inheritance.

CHAPTER 3

Design Choices, Design Flaws, and Cryptoeconomics

The design of smart contracts affects both the low-level security of the contract, and the expected properties of the system as perceived by the end user. Systems employing smart contracts must be implemented carefully to avoid common programming mistakes (for example, re-entrancy), but also designed with centralization, fairness, and cryptoeconomic concerns in mind. A user expecting a particular outcome of such a system should be confident that there are no technical issues and that the system performs as intended whenever possible, even when the code is written correctly.

In this chapter, we discuss choices that can be made when designing smart contracts that may affect external issues (such as token value, or computation correctness) in addition to introducing more complex contract code which may introduce new sources of errors. Risks associated with such choices are illustrated in detail for token sale contracts. More general concerns regarding cryptoeconomic choices of smart contract-governed protocols are discussed at a high level at the end of the chapter.

3.1 DESIGN CHOICES

A design choice is a relatively high-level decision that a smart contract author makes when developing a contract. Sample design choices may include: choosing between a capped or uncapped token sale, favoring early ICO contributors by giving them a bonus or treating all contributors equally, and choosing to make your application centralized or decentralized. Authors of smart contracts go through multiple design choices that have significant implications on how value is transferred, who can transfer value, and even why someone would be incentivized to use the given smart contract.

3.1.1   CENTRALIZED APPLICATION OR A SMART CONTRACT?

The first major question to ask before designing a smart contract is whether the blockchain is the right solution for the problem. Does it make sense to decentralize the given network application? Arguably, most of the ideas proposed during the ICO wave in 2017 do not require the blockchain at all. Many of these applications would run perfectly fine if implemented as a centralized service, and in some cases, these applications would even perform better if they were centralized. So when is the blockchain the preferred solution? Before answering this question, let us look at some of the properties of centralized network applications.

Centralized applications are hosted by a single trusted entity that owns the hardware, the software, and the users' data. If the entity disappears (for example, goes out of business), there is nobody else to continue running the service, especially if it is a proprietary application. Centralized applications have been around for decades, and, as such, they benefit from the significant efforts that were put into improving their scalability (for example, MapReduce [57]), and seamless integration with traditional financial systems via online payment processors. On the other hand, they are prone to censorship, surveillance, downtimes, and data tampering. These are some important tradeoffs that need to be considered when deciding between centralized and decentralized application architectures.

Blockchain is the right solution if the lack of trust in the third party is the primary concern: that is, when censorship, data integrity, transparency, persistence, interoperability, or privacy are non-negotiable features of the software to be built. Having these characteristics comes with an important disadvantage: decreased efficiency due to redundant data storage and computation. However, this very redundancy makes smart contracts unstoppable by default. Unless coded otherwise, they will keep operating as long as there is at least one active node on the network.

3.1.2   PRIVILEGED OWNER OR LACK OF OWNERSHIP?

Although the blockchain that runs smart contracts is decentralized by design, smart contracts can be written in a way that gives special privileges, such as ownership, to some users, but not to others. Effectively, such a design allows for centralization of power in an otherwise decentralized application. It appears to be in conflict with the decentralization philosophy that drove the development and adoption of blockchains and smart contracts. Depending on the smart contract role, however, centralization may be an unnecessary risk, or it may be a necessary and desirable characteristic. It is up to the smart contract author to decide how much influence over the smart contract should be preserved in the hands of the owner. in the following, we look at two important use cases: token contracts and token sale contracts (aka. ICO contracts).

3.1.2.1 Token Contracts

The premise of decentralized cryptocurrencies is to represent digital assets that are not controlled by any specific entity. Cryptocurrencies differ from the traditional fiat currencies issued and controlled by central banks. Token contracts comprise a subset of decentralized cryptocurrencies and represent programmable money. They are a major class of smart contracts on the Ethereum network—there are over 130,000 tokens deployed on the mainnet [59].

A typical token smart contract is a distributed ledger which maintains a map of accounts and corresponding balances (for example, see Figure 3.1), and offers (some of) the following functionalities: (1) transfer to another account, (2) approval of another account to transfer tokens on behalf of the owner, (3) minting (creating tokens), and (4) burning (destroying tokens). In our auditing practice, we recommend, as much as possible, that the contract owner has no extra privileges over these functionalities, and that cryptocurrencies stay truly decentralized to minimize

```
1  contract Coin {
2    address public creator;
3    mapping (address => uint) public balances;
4
5    function constructor(uint supply) public {
6      creator = msg.sender;
7      balances[msg.sender] = supply;
8    }
9
10   function transfer(address receiver, uint amount) public {
11     if (balances[msg.sender] >= amount) {
12       balances[msg.sender] -= amount;
13       balances[receiver] += amount;
14     }
15   }
16 }
```

Figure 3.1. Simple token contract with the transfer functionality.

Table 3.1. Examples of power centralization in token smart contracts and possible risks

Restriction	Rationale	Risk of a malicious contract owner
Owner can pause transfers at any time.	Stop token transfers if the contract gets hacked.	Prevent users from using their tokens, and render the contract useless.
Owner can whitelist and blacklist arbitrary addresses.	Limit who can transfer tokens.	Censorship.
Owner can do arbitrary transfers.	Recover tokens from a malicious actor if the contract gets hacked.	Confiscate tokens from any user at any time.
Owner can do unlimited minting.	Manual token sale at a promised rate for the incoming ether.	Arbitrarily increase the supply without respecting the agreed upon rate.
Only owner can burn tokens.	Limit who can burn tokens.	Users can burn tokens by sending them to bogus addresses, such as 0x0 without adjusting the total supply.

the risk of a malicious actor destroying the currency. We have observed contracts where designers decided otherwise. Table 3.1 summarizes some of these design choices, their rationale, and possible risks.

3.1.2.2 Token Sale Contracts

Token sale contracts (for example, see Figure 3.2) govern crowd and private sales of tokens. In these contracts, centralization of power is perfectly justified and desirable for setting up and managing the sale. A token sale is typically organized by a single entity whose goal is to raise funds, such as ether, for a specific project. This single entity is responsible for collecting the funds and offering tokens in return.

During the token sale, the owner may have extra privileges over the contract and the token. This centralization of power is only meant to be temporary, as it only pertains to the token sale contract for the duration of the sale. It may also extend to the token to enable or disable certain functionalities, such as transfers, before the sale concludes, and may

```
1   contract TokenSale {
2     address public owner;
3     address public wallet;
4     uint256 public rate;
5     uint256 public weiRaised;
6     ERC20 public token;
7
8     modifier onlyOwner() {
9       require(msg.sender == owner);
10      _;
11    }
12
13    constructor(address _wallet, uint256 _rate, ERC20 _token)
          public {
14      owner = msg.sender;
15      wallet = _wallet;
16      rate = _rate;
17      token = _token;
18    }
19
20    function () external payable {
21      uint256 weiAmount = msg.value;
22      uint256 tokenAmount = weiAmount.mul(rate);
23      weiRaised = weiRaised.add(weiAmount);
24      token.transfer(beneficiary, tokenAmount);
25      wallet.transfer(msg.value);
26    }
27
28    // only owner can change the wallet that receives the funds
29    function changeWallet(address newWallet) public onlyOwner {
30      wallet = newWallet;
31    }
32  }
```

Figure 3.2. Simple token sale contract.

also be used to couple the token with the sale contract (for example, see Figure 3.3). This coupling allows the token sale rules to be executed as a smart contract to automate the sale without any further input from the owner or third parties. When the token sale finishes (typically, it ranges from seconds to weeks), the owner is no longer privileged and the token sale contract can no longer impact the token.

3.1.3   CERTAINTY OF VALUATION OR CERTAINTY OF PARTICIPATION?

The majority of token sale contracts are constructed either as capped (for example, see Figure 3.4) or uncapped sales (for example, see Figure 3.2). A capped sale means that a fixed number of tokens is offered at a fixed price, and, consequently, the valuation is fixed. The downside of this approach is that popular capped crowdsales are often oversubscribed; their tokens sell out within seconds and few individuals are able to participate (for

```
1  contract Coin {
2    // allowance mapping
3    mapping (address => mapping (address => uint256)) private
        _allowed;
4    // the address of a sale currently selling this token
5    address public crowdSaleAddr;
6
7    modifier onlyOwner() {
8      require(msg.sender == owner);
9      _;
10   }
11
12   constructor() public {
13     owner = msg.sender;
14   }
15
16   // removes allowance from the old sale and gives it to the a
        new
17   function setSale(address _saleAddr, uint256 _amountForSale)
        external onlyOwner {
18     // if 0, then full available sale supply is assumed
19     uint amount = (_amountForSale == 0) ? crowdSaleAllowance :
        _amountForSale;
20     // clear allowance of old, and set allowance of new
21     _allowed[msg.sender][crowdSaleAddr] = 0;
22     _allowed[msg.sender][_crowdSaleAddr] = amount;
23     crowdSaleAddr = _crowdSaleAddr;
24   }
25 }
```

Figure 3.3. Excerpt from a simple token contract with a function callable only by the owner.

example, BAT token sold out within 30 seconds) [60]. Uncapped crowdsales do not have this issue as there is no cap on the accepted ether: anyone can join the crowdsale and buy tokens. The disadvantage of this approach is that participants cannot know the token valuation upfront, and, consequently, what percentage of the total supply they will own.

Interactive token sale, aka Interactive ICO (IICO) [58], is a protocol that guarantees both the certainty of valuation and the certainty of participation. It does this by carrying out the sale in multiple rounds. In each round, each user is allowed to propose a bid on how many tokens they would like to purchase and at what total cap (the caps are likely to differ between users). Consequently, the certainty of valuation is satisfied because going through the multiple sale rounds is likely to take hours (if not days). Also in each round, if the total raised ether is higher than some of the users' proposed caps, their entries are removed from bidding. Users are allowed to rejoin in the next round with a new proposal. The protocol finishes when the raised funds and the caps converge to an equilibrium.

```
1   contract CappedTokenSale {
2     address public owner;
3     address public wallet;
4     uint256 public rate;
5     uint256 public weiRaised;
6     uint256 public cap;
7     ERC20 public token;
8
9     modifier onlyOwner() {
10      require(msg.sender == owner);
11      _;
12    }
13
14    constructor(address _wallet, uint256 _rate, uint256 _cap, ERC20
          _token) public {
15      owner = msg.sender;
16      wallet = _wallet;
17      rate = _rate;
18      cap = _cap;
19      token = _token;
20    }
21
22    function () external payable {
23      uint256 weiAmount = msg.value;
24      uint256 tokenAmount = weiAmount.mul(rate);
25      weiRaised = weiRaised.add(weiAmount);
26      // ensure that the raised funds are within the cap
27      require(weiRaised <= cap);
28      token.transfer(beneficiary, tokenAmount);
29      wallet.transfer(msg.value);
30    }
31
32    // only owner can change the wallet that receives the funds
33    function changeWallet(address newWallet) public onlyOwner {
34      wallet = newWallet;
35    }
36  }
```

Figure 3.4. Simple capped token sale contract.

3.2 DESIGN FLAWS

Often, when we think of cybersecurity, we think of cryptography. However, smart contract security considers more than the mere bits and bytes of data floating about within some piece of code. A smart contract, even if functioning in a seemingly correct way on the surface, may be corrupted by even minuscule aberrations in logic. As seen in the hack of The DAO, the ordering of a few lines of code changed the course of history [2].

Everything depends on the requirements and intent of the contract. This section will delve into the various ways in which a "functioning" contract still contains vulnerabilities that undesirably alter the code's behavior.

3.2.1 PROGRESSIVE TOKEN SALE

Most crowdsale contracts, by default, release all purchased tokens to all users at a single time. What if instead, a contract progressively released tokens in portions of the total amount over a certain period of time? How would the design of this token look?

First, a list of token purchasers would need to be maintained. Second, a mapping from the purchaser to their total amount would also need to be maintained. Two functions are required: one for users to buy tokens, and another for the contract owner to pay out users. This, plus the fundamental logic from the previous token sale contracts will allow us to construct a framework for our smart contract. Figure 3.5 provides a preliminary approach to implementing this kind of token sale.

Ostensibly, all is good and well. `purchaseTokens()` contains the logic for users to purchase a certain number of tokens, and the owner can disperse the tokens gradually with `sendTokensWithRatio()` after the end of the crowdsale, a function which looks up the `beneficiaries` array, multiplies each beneficiary's balance by some ratio, subtracts the result from the beneficiary's balance, and then sends the beneficiary that amount in the actual token contract. There is, however, a major flaw with this logic which may cause the results to deviate from expectations.

Stated explicitly, the goal of this contract is to allow users to purchase a certain number of tokens proportional to the amount of ether they give to the token. The owner, at their own discretion, will call `sendTokensWithRatio()` with any ratio they would like (represented as separate `numerator` and `denominator` variables given Solidity's lack of floating point variables). Each address, by the end of the call, should only have received exactly the given ratio of tokens from their balance. Let us take a deeper dive to see how this contract subtly disobeys expectations.

Take a closer look at the `purchaseTokens()` function. Within this function, every time a user makes a purchase, their name is added to the list of beneficiaries. This seems appropriate—to track each purchase's beneficiary, add them with each call—but what happens when a single user makes multiple purchases? According to the current contract's functionality, the user's address is pushed to the end of the `beneficiaries` array *each time* the `purchaseTokens()` function is called. With this knowledge, can we come up with a specific counterexample to prove that the contract disobeys expectations?

Take a random user, Bob, who wants to purchase some tokens from this contract. Knowingly or unknowingly, by the completion of the call to `sendTokensWithRatio()`, Bob will have more than his fair share

```
1   contract ProgressiveTokenSale {
2       address public wallet;
3       uint256 public rate;
4       ERC20 public token;
5
6       mapping(address => uint256) public balances;
7       address[] beneficiaries;
8
9       modifier onlyOwner() {
10          require(msg.sender == owner);
11          _;
12      }
13
14      constructor(address _wallet, uint256 _rate, ERC20 _token)
            public {
15          wallet = _wallet;
16          rate = _rate;
17          token = _token;
18      }
19
20      function sendTokensWithRatio(uint256 _numerator, uint256
            _denominator) external onlyOwner {
21          require(_numerator <= _denominator);
22          for (uint256 i = 0; i < beneficiaries.length; i++) {
23              address beneficiary = beneficiaries[i];
24              uint256 balance = balances[beneficiary];
25              if (balance > 0) {
26                  uint256 amount = balance.mul(_numerator).div
                        (_denominator);
27                  balances[beneficiary] = balance.sub(amount);
28                  token.transfer(beneficiary, amount);
29              }
30          }
31      }
32
33      function purchaseTokens() public payable {
34          uint256 _tokenAmount = weiAmount.mul(rate);
35          beneficiaries.push(msg.sender);
36          balances[msg.sender] = balances[msg.sender].add
                (_tokenAmount);
37      }
38  }
```

Figure 3.5. A contract delivering tokens in portions rather than all at once.

of tokens distributed to him early. Suppose Bob wants to purchase 200 tokens. He calls purchaseTokens() with an appropriate amount of ether, and the contract adds his address to the list of beneficiaries. A few days later, he decides he wants to purchase another 200 tokens to get a total of 400 in his balance. He calls purchaseTokens() once more with the same amount of ether, and his address is added to the list of beneficiaries again. What's the issue here?

Let's say that the owner decides after Bob's second token purchase to distribute half of each beneficiary's tokens by calling sendTokens

WithRatio(1,2). Based on the design of sendTokensWithRatio(), the entire beneficiaries array is examined. As a reminder: for each member, their balance is multiplied by the effective ratio. The product is subtracted from their account in the token sale contract, then sent to their account in the actual token contract. When Bob's address shows up the first time during the loop within sendTokensWithRatio(), his balance will be 400 tokens. The amount which will be transferred from the token sale contract to the token contract is exactly one half of 400, or 200 tokens. This amount is subtracted from his balance then transferred to him via the token contract. Now, Bob has received 200 tokens and still has 200 more waiting in his balance to be distributed. However, there is a catch: because Bob called purchaseTokens() twice, his address will appear *again in the same call* within the beneficiaries array. Before the loop finishes, his address' balance will be loaded again, now 200. Half of 200, or 100, will be subtracted from his balance and sent to him, making for the second transaction to Bob within a single call to sendTokensWithRatio()! By the end of the loop, Bob has now received a total of *300 tokens*. Even the owner only expected him to receive 200, because Bob's address was saved more than once within the list of beneficiaries, and no measure in sendTokensWithRatio() or elsewhere checked for duplicates. Though the contract code contains no vulnerabilities, the *design of the contract itself* deviated from expectations.

So how can we fix this problem?

One possible fix is to prevent an address from being added twice to the beneficiaries array in the first place by placing a condition within purchaseTokens() before adding to the array to prevent duplicates. It's known that the first time a user calls purchaseTokens(), their balance will be 0. To ensure a user is added *exactly once*, it then follows that their address is pushed to the beneficiaries array *if and only if* their current balance is zero.

One might think all problems have now been solved. However, even with this provision, an issue remains: what if a sly attacker sends multiple calls to purchaseTokens with a msg.value of 0? Their balance will remain at 0, but their address will still get added to the list for each call, deviating from the contract's desired functionality. To mitigate this sneaky hack, a second condition must also be true: msg.value > 0. This condition will stop attackers from repeatedly adding themselves to the list. Additionally, this provision does not interfere with honest behavior, since there is no reasonable scenario where an honest user would call a purchaseTokens() function with no ether attached. Figure 3.6 demonstrates how to modify purchaseTokens() to enforce these conditions.

```
1  contract ProgressiveTokenSale {
2     ...
3
4     function purchaseTokens() public payable {
5        if (msg.value > 0 && balances[msg.sender] == 0) {
6           beneficiaries.push(_beneficiary);
7        }
8        uint256 _tokenAmount = weiAmount.mul(rate);
9        beneficiaries.push(msg.sender);
10       balances[msg.sender] = balances[msg.sender].add(
             _tokenAmount);
11    }
12 }
```

Figure 3.6. A correctly implemented version of the progressive token sale contract.

From the bits and bytes to the overall design, the iterative process of examining smart contract implementation further demonstrates the principle of security as a spectrum rather than a black or white state. To cement this idea, here's a twist: believe it or not, there is *still* an issue with this contract depending on how the owner uses it. Granted, the issue is one that can be considered an edge case and possibly out of the scope of the owner's concerns, but the anomalous functionality nevertheless exists.

The issue arises if the owner distributes all the tokens, that is, makes a call of sendTokensWithRatio(1, 1), before the end of the crowdsale. If this happens, any user who called purchaseTokens() before the owner's call to sendTokensWithRatio() will be added to the beneficiaries array once more with another token purchase call to the contract, as their balance was reset to 0 by the owner's call and will satisfy the condition for being added into the contract. To fix this, one can clear the beneficiaries array each time all tokens are distributed. Each solution often comes another broken assumption and another security vulnerability to consider.

3.3 CRYPTOECONOMICS

Cryptoeconomics is a widely used term in the blockchain space that describes the economics of cryptographic protocols on blockchains. It is an important concept, as many protocols developed in this space are not provably secure, but secure simply because it would be cost prohibitive to attack the system.

The first example of this is a proof-of-work blockchain such as Bitcoin or Ethereum. Although the cryptographic protocols that govern the operation of the chain are believed to be secure, such as ECDSA and the hash functions used, either chain is still susceptible to an attack by incredibly wealthy actors. Recall from Chapter 2 that both of these blockchains enforce the addition of new blocks onto a canonical chain. An actor with an unlimited source of funds can exploit this behavior. In particular, the attacker can use their unlimited wealth to increase computational power so that they are able to compute more proof-of-work hashes than the rest of the network combined. At a given point in time, the attacker can start to mine additional blocks from some block on the network, say b_i, and mine new blocks on top of each previous block that they mine. By *withholding* these new blocks mined until they have a suitably large chain that is longer than the publicly available canonical chain, they can cause economic unrest. Unrest occurs if they announce their blocks on the network, which propagate over it automatically. Future blocks—even those mined by honest actors— are required to be appended to this new chain, and so any blocks appended to b_i on the public chain are now orphaned. In particular, transfers of funds to users included in those blocks and miner rewards for those blocks are no longer valid. If users of the network wished to spend funds collected in the newly orphaned blocks, they are no longer able to do so.

If an attacker has 51 percent of the computation power used to compute hashes on a network, they can cause issues. This is a well-documented threat to most proof-of-work blockchains, and one that is not necessarily being countered actively [61].

Although possible, these types of attacks are unlikely because they are incredibly expensive. To match the current miner hash power for Bitcoin, several server farms would be required, each with thousands of ASIC chips or GPUs, both of which are costly. In addition, as more honest members join the network, the number of processors required by the attacker also increases. Additionally, if a network was comprised in this manner, honest users may abandon the network. In this case, controlling the network is less desirable for the attacker: the funds it mines will have less utility, and fewer people will accept them.

With this in mind, we say that a network like Bitcoin or Ethereum is *cryptoeconomically secure*. There are flaws, but they are unlikely to occur because actors are rational, and such an attack will very likely cost more than any gain.

Cryptoeconomic security is not limited to the first layer (the blockchain itself). The application layer must also be secured against irrational actors, especially if it is the case that decentralized actors are responsible for taking actions or fulfilling special roles for which they are rewarded. These concerns are best illustrated through use cases.

3.3.1 CRYPTOECONOMICS OF THE TRUEBIT PROTOCOL

TrueBit [44] is a protocol for scaling computation on the Ethereum network. Due to the gas limitations of the Ethereum network (see Chapter 2), Ethereum smart contracts are unable to perform large computations. Additionally, some computations within the gas limits may still have a high cost to compute on-chain if gas prices are high. TrueBit aims to tackle these concerns by incentivizing actors to perform computations off-chain; that is, on their own system, and submitting only the (correct) results to the chain.

In a trusted setting, this is somewhat trivial. If a user cannot perform a computation locally or on-chain, they could pay a service like Amazon AWS, upload their code, and receive a result in due time. On the other hand, if Amazon cannot be trusted, this scenario becomes difficult: what if Amazon changed their computation environment, and the result is not the one that is expected?

TrueBit includes cryptoeconomic systems to discourage this behavior, which are implemented through a system of user deposits and on-chain adjudication of small computations.

In TrueBit, a user S submits a task T which is to be computed for a reward that they specify. Users who have computational power can run T and submit (the hash of) their results to the TrueBit smart contract, along with a deposit. Suppose some user U submits a result u. Another user can recompute the result and determine whether or not they want to challenge the submitted result. If they get the same result, they will not; if they get a different answer, they should challenge. This user is called a verifier and if they challenge, is required to submit a deposit and their result v (note that $v \neq u$). The TrueBit smart contract can then query small program states from both U and the verifier V, to find where computation diverged: they received the same input, so there is some common point, and they computed different outputs, so they diverged. The contract finds the largest common prefix of the computations u and v, so that the application of the next single operation results in the divergence. This single operation is small enough to be executed on-chain, and since the Ethereum network can be trusted, the result is taken as correct. The user which submitted the correct result is awarded the deposit of the other user, as well as the reward promised by S.

With this simple description, the TrueBit protocol is already immensely interesting and useful. Of course, there are some limitations: TrueBit requires S to submit tasks which conform to some properties, for example, T must be written in some particular language like Rust, and T must be deterministic. For many applications, these limitations are reasonable. However, a careful analysis of the protocol's operation (as described earlier) reveals a subtle flaw.

In TrueBit as described previously, assuming the first 1,000,000 tasks are computed by honest solvers, verifiers are no longer incentivized to participate. Verifiers are only rewarded if they catch a malicious solver; if there are none, they repeat computations effectively without purpose, and at the loss of the cost of gas invoking the transactions to send their results to the protocol contract and the energy costs associated with running the computations. Thus, over time, a rational verifier may realize that a loss of funds is occurring and cease to participate in the protocol. At this point, a solver's work goes unchecked, and is reported as correct (since it was unchallenged), even if it is incorrect. Of course, with only a single honest verifier, a malicious solver may not be guaranteed success, but if the result of the computation also benefits them, they may be willing to try. And if there are more malicious actors than honest verifiers, incorrect computations will be marked as correct.

TrueBit takes a lesson from poker to solve this problem. In poker, if you never bluff, your opponents will always wait for a confident hand, and you will lose more often. If you bluff occasionally, you keep your opponent guessing and they cannot count on your behavior to guide their betting strategy. The same principle is applied by TrueBit. Occasionally, it will *require* a solver to submit an invalid result so that a challenge is warranted. Additionally, by collecting fees from all transactions that contribute to a large jackpot, a verifier who wins these specific *forced errors* can be rewarded with a large value, incentivizing their liveliness on the protocol even if these are rare. The technical methods for implementing this are interesting, but too lengthy to discuss here. See the TrueBit whitepaper for more details [44].

In summary, even though the original description of TrueBit—without forced errors—may be implemented correctly, users of the system may eventually suffer from the choices made by omitting a mechanic like forced errors. Design choices for decentralized applications introduce attack vectors that can be more complex than exploiting an error in the smart contract itself.

3.3.2   CRYPTOECONOMICS OF THE ASTRAEA ORACLE

For some problems, the only decentralized solutions we have rely on cryptoeconomics in order to operate correctly. One such problem is that of an *oracle*: a protocol that brings information that exists in the real world onto a blockchain [62]. A trivial centralized service is possible: pay someone to put a representation of that information on-chain, and if they are trustworthy, the result is accurate. However, in decentralized systems for which information must be repeatedly imported to the blockchain from off-chain, a decentralized oracle is required. An oracle may also be considered a special use case of the computation problem solved by True-Bit, but this analogy is awkward. In particular, the representation of data may not be deterministic, and the computation involved is not necessarily resource-intensive; therefore, there is value in exploring this protocol as an example.

Astraea [63] is a decentralized oracle that relies on cryptoecomics to operate correctly. In this protocol, a submitter submits a proposition that is either true or false, with a bounty that is awarded for determining which of these it is. Voters vote on whether the result is true or false. Certifiers add additional support for the result by placing a large stake in its correctness.

A voter plays a role by staking a small amount, and earning a small amount in return. They are randomly assigned to vote on propositions, and stakes are placed before a proposition assignment. The stake commits them to voting for a proposition, regardless of the end result. If they vote correctly (determined at the end of the protocol), they get a share of the sum of deposits that voted correctly, taken from the bounty provided by the submitter.

A certifier stakes a large amount in order to certify that a proposition is either true or false, staking on propositions of their choice. This means some propositions may never be certified. Careful reward pools are crucial to distribute the chosen propositions uniformly from the true propositions and the false ones.

At the end of the protocol, the outcome with the biggest majority of stakes (deposits from voters, and deposits from certifiers) is the result, unless there is a tie. In the case of a tie, the outcome is unknown, so while the voters are not penalized, the certifiers lose their stake.

With careful parameter tuning, Astraea makes it arbitrarily difficult for an adversary to force an incorrect result. The proof is technical and can be found in the paper [63]. Without careful tuning, the protocol may produce incorrect data, driving users away. Consequently, design choices must take care to ensure any parameters in a contract are appropriate.

CHAPTER 4

COMMON SECURITY FLAWS

This chapter discusses common security flaws in smart contracts. The vulnerabilities discussed are based on real-world attacks that in the past resulted in the loss of ether and other tokens, our own experiences with manual auditing of smart contracts, as well as theoretical attacks described by the researchers [81, 116], developers and auditors [77].

Despite the chapter referring to smart contracts on the Ethereum network, the described flaws and respective attacks can be generally applicable to smart contracts developed for other blockchains as well. Developers should be cognizant of these issues when developing smart contracts, new blockchains, virtual machines and programming languages.

This chapter is mainly aimed at developers and makes liberal use of code samples to provide concrete examples of vulnerabilities, exploits, and fixes. However, we've done our best to explain vulnerabilities' mechanism of action and impact in plain English when possible, so that managers, executives, and other readers who may not have a programming background may still find value in skimming through this chapter.

4.1 TRANSACTIONS ON ETHEREUM IN DEPTH

The Ethereum network can be seen as a state machine. The change of state is triggered by transactions submitted to the network by users. Therefore, it should not be surprising that the common security flaws of smart contracts are transaction-oriented. To properly understand these flaws and vulnerabilities, we need to understand the Ethereum transactions in detail first.

Each Ethereum transaction is a data payload that consists of several parameters that are encoded and broadcasted to the network. These parameters are:

- `nonce`: a number that determines how many transactions were broadcasted by the sender before this transaction. It uniquely identifies the order of transactions sent by the same sender, and it is used to avoid repeated execution of transactions.
- `gasPrice`: relates to the concept of *gas*. *Gas* is a virtual currency unit that the sender needs to pay for executing a transaction that modifies the state of the blockchain. Every instruction in the EVM specifies how much gas the user has to pay for its execution. `gasPrice` then determines how much ether the user is willing to pay for 1 gas. This can be any non-negative number, including 0. The total price of the transaction in ether is then determined by multiplying the `gasPrice` by the cost of all executed instructions.
- `data`: an optional string of bytes that encodes the smart contract method called by this transaction and the arguments passed to the call.
- `value`: an optional number that determines how much ether is sent along with this transaction.
- `chainId`: a constant numeric identifier of the Ethereum network that allows for distinguishing the Ethereum network (ETH) from other Ethereum-based networks such as Ethereum Classic (ETC). The *chainId* of ETH is 1.
- `v, r, s`: cryptographic values that determine the transaction signature. From these, one can derive the public key of the sender, and from the public key, one can derive the Ethereum address of the sender.

Two more pieces of information are important when it comes to creating Ethereum transactions, but they are not encoded in the transaction payload itself:

- `to`: an address in the Ethereum network that determines the recipient of the transaction. If the purpose of the transaction is creating a new smart contract, the recipient is the special address `0x0`. Another special recipient is the address `0xdead` that is used for burning ether.
- `gasLimit`: how much gas a user is willing to purchase for executing the transaction. If the total amount of gas needed to execute the transaction exceeds the gasLimit, the transaction fails and the state of the chain is reverted.

When a user generates a transaction, they specify the value for all the aforementioned fields, sign the transaction using their private key, and submit it to an Ethereum node. The node verifies that the transaction is valid and broadcasts it to the network. The separation of signing from broadcasting allows transactions to be signed on an off-line machine and transferred to a different on-line machine (for example via USB or a QR code) for broadcasting.

When the transaction gets broadcasted, it becomes part of the so-called *mempool* of transactions. The miners then select transactions from the mempool and organize them into a block using proof of work. The new block is then appended to the chain and the transaction becomes part of the blockchain.

Each Ethereum node maintains the state of the network. This state captures a mapping of each account address to its ether balance, nonce, storage, and program code (the last two are only used by smart contracts). When an Ethereum node receives a new block mined by a miner, it reads the transactions contained in that block and interprets them using the Ethereum Virtual Machine (EVM). This interpretation changes the state of Ethereum as it is understood by that individual node. Since Ethereum maintains consensus on its blockchain, the state changes propagate through the network until all nodes then maintain the same state.

This basic introduction allows us to describe some common vulnerabilities and security flaws of smart contracts. We will elaborate on the relevant nuances of the EVM, transaction representation, and execution in the following sections. We refer the reader to Chapter 2 or [65] for a more thorough explanation of how Ethereum works.

4.2 INTEGER OVERFLOWS AND UNDERFLOWS

Integer overflows and underflows are well-known in digital systems. Numbers are represented as sequences of bits that have limited length. As the number of bits is limited (in Solidity and EVM, the limit is up to 256 bits), the range of numbers that can be represented is limited as well. This can create unintended consequences (which can be exploited) if the number stored in a variable is higher than the maximum or lower than the minimum.

4.2.1 MECHANISM

One can easily understand an overflow by imagining an odometer exceeding its maximum—it will wrap around and start counting back from 0 (see Figure 4.1). When the number is too large, the same thing happens with the binary representation of numbers in the EVM—they roll over the maximum for the given data type and become the minimum for the type.

Figure 4.1. Illustration of an integer overflow on an odometer.

This minimum is 0 for the unsigned integers and the most negative representable number for signed types. Integer underflow is an analogous issue where the odometer rolls backwards—it wraps around 0 to its maximum. This would be the case for unsigned types. For signed types, the representation would wrap around the most negative number.

Figure 4.2 shows a smart contract vulnerable to integer underflows. It presents a naive implementation of approve(), a method required by the ERC20 token standard (which will be in depth discussed in Section 4.3). *Approval* is a mechanism for allowing third party users transfer funds from accounts, and approve() sets limits for such transfers. For reasons discussed in Section 4.3, the community also recommends implementing the methods increaseAllowance() and decreaseAllowance(). The OpenZeppelin framework [66] currently includes these methods in their implementation of the ERC20 standard.

If spender convinces the account owner to send a transfer that decreases the spender's allowance below 0, in this implementation, the spender will receive an astronomical allowance that will likely enable them to withdraw the entire balance of the account. In such a scenario, Alice, who owns 1,000,000 tokens, approves spender Mallory for 15 tokens. Later she decreases Mallory's allowance by 16. The value in approvals[msg.sender][spender] representing Mallory's allowance suffers an underflow and becomes $2^{256} - 1$. Mallory now can withdraw all of Alice's tokens.

4.2.1.1 *Example*

An example of the integer overflow vulnerability is presented in Figure 4.3. The smart contract represents an imaginary tokenization of a gold trading

```
1   contract AwesomeToken {
2
3     // Holds allowances for ERC20 method transferFrom()
4     // token owner => (spender => allowance)
5     mapping (address => mapping (address => uint256)) public
          approvals;
6     ...
7
8     // Sets an allowance for the spender to withdraw tokens
9     // from the account of msg.sender
10    function approve(address spender, uint256 n) public returns(
          bool) {
11      approvals[msg.sender][spender] = n;
12      return true;
13    }
14
15    // Decreases the allowance for the spender to
16    // withdraw tokens from the account of msg.sender by value n
17    function decreaseAllowance(address spender, uint256 n) public
          returns(bool) {
18      uint256 approvedNow = approvals[msg.sender][spender];
19      approvals[msg.sender][spender] = approvedNow - n;
20      return true;
21    }
22    ...
23
24  }
```

Figure 4.2. A smart contract vulnerable to integer underflow.

```
1   contract GoldInventory {
2
3     // Records the number of gold bars owned by users
4     mapping (address => uint256) public goldBars;
5
6     // Records the user token balances
7     mapping (address => uint256) public balances;
8     ...
9
10    // Converts gold bars of the sender into tokens while giving
11    // a commission to the contract
12    function sell(uint256 bars, uint256 commission) public {
13      address contractAddress = address(this);
14      require(goldBars[msg.sender] >= bars + commission);
15
16      goldBars[msg.sender] = goldBars[msg.sender] - (bars +
            commission);
17      goldBars[contractAddress] = goldBars[contractAddress] +
            commission;
18      balances[msg.sender] = balances[msg.sender] + bars;
19      balances[contractAddress] = balances[contractAddress] - bars;
20    }
21
22  }
```

Figure 4.3. A smart contract vulnerable to integer overflow.

business. The business holds both physical gold bars and cash represented by tokens. The users can exchange gold bars (recorded in the attribute goldBars) for tokens (recorded in the attribute balances) and vice versa. For the simplicity of the contract, we assume that the rate is always 1:1. For the exchange of bars for tokens, the contract exposes the `sell()` method. The user can specify an arbitrary number of gold bars that the contract owner receives as a commission for their services.

Note that both the fields `bars` and `commission` are parameters provided by the user. Therefore, they can have arbitrary values. If Mallory calls the `sell()` method with parameters `bars` = $2^{256} - 1$ and `commission` = 1, the sum on line 16 overflows and becomes 0. Therefore, it will pass the check. As a result of this, the smart contract will record the wrong balances in its internal state. After the execution of this method:

- Mallory will own the same number of gold bricks as she did before, because `bars + commission = 0`.
- Assuming that Mallory's balance was 0 before executing this code, it will now be $2^{256} - 1$.
- The contract will own 1 additional gold bar that was passed to it as a commission if it owned less than $2^{256} - 1$ bars before executing the code, and will own 0 gold bars if it had exactly $2^{256} - 1$ bars.
- Due to the integer underflow, the contract will assume that its balance increased by 1 token if it was less than $2^{256} - 1$ before executing the code, and it will be 0 if it was exactly $2^{256} - 1$.

Mallory is now free to use her astronomical balance as she pleases.

4.2.1.2 Prevention

The best way of avoiding integer underflows and overflows is checking that the results of arithmetic operations are valid. For example, if two unsigned integers a and b are added together, the result $a + b$ should be greater or equal to a. If an overflow occurs, this property is violated.

The OpenZeppelin framework contains the library `SafeMath` that has safe versions of arithmetic operations of unsigned integers which ensure that the results are valid (for the code of the `SafeMath` library, we refer readers to the OpenZeppelin Github repository [66]). Developers can use these functions to prevent integer underflows and overflows. A safe implementation of the gold inventory contract using `SafeMath` arithmetic functions is shown in Figure 4.4.

Integer overflow and underflow vulnerabilities can be detected by automated tools for smart contract analysis. Unfortunately, these tools often report false positives (see Chapter 5 for more details). In order to

```
1    contract GoldInventorySafe {
2
3      using SafeMath for uint256;
4
5      // Records the number of gold bars owned by users
6      mapping (address => uint256) public goldBars;
7
8      // Records the user's token balances
9      mapping (address => uint256) public balances;
10     ...
11
12     // Converts gold bars of the sender into tokens while giving
13     // a commission to the contract
14     function sell(uint256 bars, uint256 commission) public {
15       address contractAddress = address(this);
16       require(goldBars[msg.sender] >= bars.add(commission));
17
18       goldBars[msg.sender] = goldBars[msg.sender].sub(bars.add(
             commission));
19       goldBars[contractAddress] = goldBars[contractAddress].add(
             commission);
20       balances[msg.sender] = balances[msg.sender].add(bars);
21       balances[contractAddress] = balances[contractAddress].sub(
             bars);
22     }
23   }
```

Figure 4.4. The gold inventory smart contract safe for integer underflows.

distinguish a false positive from a real issue, a proper understanding of this vulnerability is necessary.

4.3 RACE CONDITIONS IN ERC20

Because of a lack of synchronization primitives in Solidity and Ethereum, race conditions may occur with transactions. One of the most common potentials for a race condition exists in the ERC20 standard.

4.3.1 THE ERC20 STANDARD

The Ethereum community publishes recognized standards called ERCs. These standards usually specify APIs of contracts with some standard purpose. Probably the most frequently quoted ERC is ERC20 [64] that became a standard for issuing tokens on the Ethereum network. ERC20 specifies that every token should support methods:

- totalSupply() — Returns the total token supply.
- balanceOf() — Returns the balance of an account.
- transfer() — Sends tokens to another address.

- `transferFrom()` – Send tokens from one address to another. Used to allow contracts to send tokens on someone's behalf, for example, to "deposit" to a contract address and/or to charge fees in sub-currencies. The command should fail if the "from" account has not deliberately authorized the sender of the message to transfer tokens via `approve()`.
- `approve()` – Allow a spender to withdraw from the account of the message sender, possibly multiple times, up to the specified amount. If this method is called multiple times it overwrites the current allowance each time.
- `allowance()` – Returns the amount which the spender is still allowed to withdraw from the owner's account.

The signatures and semantics of the methods `totalSupply()`, `balanceOf()`, `transfer()`, `transferFrom()`, `approve()`, and `allowance()` are shown in Figure 4.5. The standard also specifies events `Approval` and `Transfer` for logging purposes. See [64] for more details.

```
1
2  contract ERC20 {
3
4     // Returns the total token supply
5     function totalSupply() constant returns (uint256 totalSupply);
6
7     // Returns the account balance of another account with address
8     // _owner
9     function balanceOf(address _owner) constant returns (uint256
           balance);
10
11    // Sends _value amount of tokens to address _to
12    function transfer(address _to, uint256 _value) returns (bool
           success);
13
14    // Send _value amount of tokens from address _from to address
15    // _to
16    function transferFrom(address _from, address _to, uint256
           _value) returns (bool success);
17
18    // Allow _spender to withdraw from your account, multiple
19    // times, up to the _value amount.
20    function approve(address _spender, uint256 _value) returns (
           bool success);
21
22    // Returns the amount which _spender is still allowed to
23    // withdraw from _owner.
24    function allowance(address _owner, address _spender) constant
           returns (uint256 remaining);
25 }
```

Figure 4.5. The interface defined by the ERC20 standard.

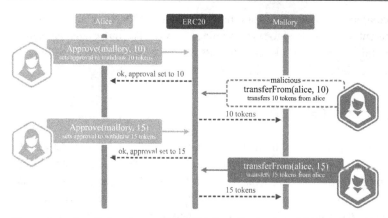

Figure 4.6. A malicious transaction of Mallory (in the dotted frame) that takes advantage of the double withdrawal exploit of ERC20.

Consider now the following scenario illustrated in Figure 4.6. Alice has a wallet and wants to allow Mallory to withdraw 10 tokens as a payment for the great piece of code that Mallory implemented for Alice's project, so she approves Mallory for 10 tokens. Mallory then talks to Alice and convinces her that she should receive a bonus of 5 tokens for the great work she did. Alice therefore sets Mallory's approval to 15 tokens. However, just before she sends the transaction, Mallory calls `transferFrom()` to withdraw her 10 tokens. She then receives an approval for another 15 tokens and withdraws all of them too.

This is called a *double withdrawal exploit*. It is caused by a race condition and lack of synchronization primitives in Solidity and Ethereum. Without additional effort, it is not possible for Alice to ensure that another transaction will not be inserted between the transactions that modify the allowance.

4.3.2 Prevention

The ERC20 standard is well known to contain this race condition and it is recommended that token owners reset allowance to 0 before setting a new value. However, this is a best practice that is not part of the standard itself. Another frequently used approach is to implement specific, safe methods for increasing and decreasing allowance.

4.4 RE-ENTRANCY

Computer scientists say that a procedure is *re-entrant* if its execution can be interrupted in the middle, initiated over (re-entered), and both runs can complete without any errors. In the context of Ethereum smart contracts, re-entrancy can lead to serious vulnerabilities. The most famous example of this was the DAO Hack. The ERC827 token standard also exhibits this vulnerability [67, 68] and is currently deemed unsafe.

4.4.1 MECHANISM

An example of a re-entrant process can be sending an e-mail. A user can start typing an e-mail using their favorite client, save a draft, send another e-mail, and finish the message later. This is a harmless example. However, imagine a poorly constructed online banking system for issuing wire transfers where the account balance is checked only at the initialization step. A user could initiate several transfers without actually submitting any of them. The banking system would confirm that the user's account holds a sufficient balance for each individual transfer. If there was no additional check at the time of the actual submission, the user could then submit all transactions and potentially exceed the balance of their account. This is the main mechanism of the re-entrancy exploit which was used in the well-known DAO hack.

4.4.2 REAL-WORLD EXAMPLE—THE DAO HACK

The DAO was a popular decentralized investment fund based on smart contracts. In 2016, the DAO smart contract accumulated over $150,000,000 (at the time) of ether. If a project that requested funding received sufficient support from the DAO community, that project's Ethereum address could withdraw ether from DAO (Figure 4.7). Unfortunately

```
1   contract BasicDAO {
2
3     mapping (address => uint) public balances;
4     ...
5
6     // transfer the entire balance of the caller of this function
7     // to the caller
8     function withdrawBalance() public {
9       bool result = msg.sender.call.value(balances[msg.sender])();
10      if (!result) {
11        throw;
12      }
13      // update balance of the withdrawer.
14      balances[msg.sender] = 0;
15    }
16  }
```

Figure 4.7. A simplified DAO contract with re-entrancy vulnerability in its withdrawBalance() method.

for the DAO, the transfer mechanism would transfer the ether to the external address before updating its internal state and noting that the balance was already transferred. This gave the attackers a recipe for withdrawing more ether than they were eligible for from the contract via re-entrancy.

The DAO hack took advantage of Ethereum's fallback function to perform a re-entrancy attack. Every Ethereum smart contract byte code contains the so-called default fallback function which has the following default implementation shown in Figure 4.8.

This default fallback function can contain arbitrary code if the developer overrides the default implementation. If it is overridden as payable, the smart contract can accept ether. The function is executed whenever ether is transferred to the contract (see the description of methods send(), transfer() and call() below) or whenever a transaction attempts to call a method that the smart contract does not implement.

At the time of writing this book, aside from calling payable methods, Solidity supports three ways of transferring ether between wallets and smart contracts. These supported methods of transferring ether are send(), transfer() and call.value(). The methods differ by how much gas they pass to the transfer for executing other methods (in case the recipient is a smart contract), and by how they handle exceptions. send() and call(). value() will merely return false upon failure but transfer() will throw an exception which will also revert state to what it was before the function call. These methods are summarized in Table 4.1.

```
1  contract EveryContract {
2
3    function () public {
4    }
5  }
```

Figure 4.8. The default implementation of the default fallback.

Table 4.1. Methods for transferring ether. By default, all the remaining gas is available when using call.value(), but the developer may choose to reduce the amount

	address. send()	address. transfer()	address. call.value()
Adjustable gas	no	no	yes
Gas limit	2300	2300	all/settable
Behavior on error	return false	throw exception	return false

In the case of the DAO smart contract, the ether was transferred using the `call.value()` method. That allowed the transfer to use the maximum possible gas limit and also prevented reverting the state upon possible exceptions. Thus, the attackers were able to create a sequence of recursive calls to siphon off funds from the DAO using a smart contract similar to the one presented in Figure 4.9.

The result was the following sequence of actions (also depicted in Figure 4.10):

1. The proxy smart contract would ask for a legitimate withdrawal.
2. The transfer from BasicDAO to the proxy smart contract triggered a fallback function.
3. The proxy smart contract fallback function would ask BasicDAO for another withdrawal.
4. The transfer from BasicDAO to the proxy smart contract triggered a fallback function.
5. The proxy smart contract fallback function would ask BasicDAO for another withdrawal.
6. ...

```
1  contract Proxy {
2
3      // Owner's address //
4      address public owner;
5
6      // Constructs the contract and stores the owner. //
7      constructor() public {
8          owner = msg.sender;
9      }
10
11     // Initiates the balance withdrawal. //
12     function callWithdrawBalance(address _address) public {
13         BasicDAO(_address).withdrawBalance();
14     }
15
16     // Fallback function for this contract.
17     // If the balance of this contract is less than 999999 Ether,
18     // triggers another withdrawal from the DAO.
19     function () public payable {
20         if (address(this).balance < 999999 ether) {
21             callWithdrawBalance(msg.sender);
22         }
23     }
24
25     // Allows the owner to get Ether from this contract. //
26     function drain() public {
27         owner.transfer(address(this).balance);
28     }
29 }
```

Figure 4.9. A smart contract for exploiting re-entrancy in BasicDAO from Figure 4.10.

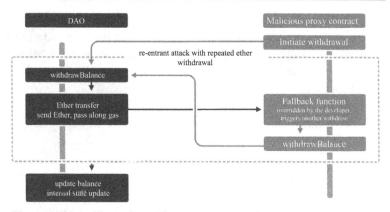

Figure 4.10. An illustration of the re-entrancy attack.

Note that the balance of the proxy smart contract was never updated (this happens after the transfer). Furthermore, notice that unless the transfer to the proxy contract fails, an exception is never thrown and the state never gets reverted.

4.4.3 PREVENTION

The re-entrancy attack in the DAO contract could have been avoided in several ways. Using the functions `send()` or `transfer()` instead of `call.value()` would not allow for recursive withdrawal calls due to the low gas stipend. Manually limiting the amount of gas passed to `call.value()` would achieve the same result.

Yet, there is a much simpler best practice that makes any re-entrancy attack impossible. Note that the DAO contract updates the user balance after the ether transfer. If this was done prior to the transfer, any recursive withdraw call would attempt to transfer a balance of 0 ether. This principle applies generally—if no internal state updates happen after an ether transfer or an external function call inside a method, the method is safe from the re-entrancy vulnerability. This makes re-entrancy vulnerabilities relatively easy to detect by automated tools (see Chapter 5 for more details).

4.5 TRANSACTION-ORDERING DEPENDENCE (TOD) AND FRONT RUNNING

The order of processing transactions on Ethereum is determined by the miners. Malicious miners may exploit this power to order transactions in ways that are beneficial to themselves.

When a transaction is submitted, it goes to the *mempool*. The miners then select transactions from the mempool and organize them into a block using proof-of-work. Once a miner mines a block, it broadcasts that new block to the network.

There are two risks that should be taken into account here:

1. The transactions are visible in mempool before they are mined.
2. The order of transactions is entirely up to miners' discretion.

Consider the contract in Figure 4.11 that enables a secure transfer of ether from the contract creator to an anonymous recipient. The contract creator specifies a hash of a secret upon creating the contract with some ether balance. The recipient proves their identity by providing a secret that hashes to the correct value. If they can do so, they will receive the balance of the contract.

First, consider a situation where the secret value is known to several users. All of them can claim the contract balance at once by submitting a transaction and become a contender for the contract balance. The real recipient will be determined by the miners who organize the transactions to the blocks. If all transactions were submitted at the same time, this would most likely be the transaction with the highest gas price.

Second, consider another situation where there is only one user who knows the secret value. They submit a transaction attempting to claim the balance. This transaction is first validated by the user's Ethereum node and then broadcasted to the network of other nodes and miners. It now resides in mempool and waits for being picked by a miner and placed in a block. This can take some time, especially if the network is congested.

Since the mempool can be read by anyone, the secret is completely exposed. Any user can decide to submit a transaction of their own and

```
1   contract SecureTransfer {
2
3     bytes32 public secretHash;
4
5     constructor(bytes32 hash) public payable {
6       secretHash = hash;
7     }
8
9     function claim(string secret) public {
10      bytes32 submittedHash = keccak256(abi.encodePacked(secret));
11      require(submittedHash == secretHash);
12      msg.sender.transfer(address(this).balance);
13    }
14  }
```

Figure 4.11. A contract for facilitating safe transfers.

compete for the contract balance, potentially with a much higher gas price. Once again, we find ourselves in the first scenario and the real recipient will be determined by the miners.

4.6 TIMESTAMP DEPENDENCE

Similar in concept to transaction ordering, miners also have control over transaction timestamps. In certain cases, such as with the Governmental Ponzi scheme, miners may be incentivized to manipulate timestamps for financial gain.

4.6.1 MECHANISM

Recall that all the transactions on Ethereum are processed by miners. The miners pick transactions from the mempool. If sufficiently incentivized, nothing prevents them from excluding transactions from blocks at will, or slightly manipulating the information about blocks mined as follows. Miners who successfully mine a block provide the timestamp of when the block was mined. The timestamps need to be increasing and cannot be too distant into the future as they would be rejected by the network nodes. However, in order to allow for some time synchronization delay, the network has a certain level of tolerance. This tolerance is not explicitly specified in the Ethereum Yellow Paper [24], but it is currently estimated to up to 15 seconds [78] based on the implementations of the most popular Ethereum nodes. Thus, miners who are incentivized to do so may manipulate timestamps.

4.6.2 REAL WORLD EXAMPLE: GOVERNMENTAL

A Ponzi scheme called GovernMental was a smart contract that contained several security flaws. The most famous one was a linked list that grew to the size that for iterating needed more gas than a block limit allows, resulting in a DoS attack on this smart contract. This is discussed in detail in Section 4.7. For the purposes of this section, we focus on the possibility of manipulating timestamps by the miners.

A simplified version of the smart contract is shown in Figure 4.12. The principle of the scheme is that users could invest ether, part of which would be added to the jackpot pool. Any user could call method resetInvestment() which will verify if at least one minute elapsed since the last investment, and if so, transfer the jackpot to the last investor.

```
1  contract Governmental {
2
3     address public owner;
4     address public lastInvestor;
5     uint public jackpot = 1 ether;
6     uint public lastInvestmentTimestamp;
7     uint public ONE_MINUTE = 1 minutes;
8
9     constructor() public payable {
10       owner = msg.sender;
11       if (msg.value < 1 ether) revert();
12    }
13
14    function invest() public payable {
15       if (msg.value < jackpot / 2) revert();
16       lastInvestor = msg.sender;
17       jackpot += msg.value / 2;
18       lastInvestmentTimestamp = block.timestamp;
19    }
20
21    function resetInvestment() public {
22       if (block.timestamp < lastInvestmentTimestamp + ONE_MINUTE) {
23         revert();
24       }
25       lastInvestor.send(jackpot);
26       owner.send(this.balance - 1 ether);
27       lastInvestor = 0;
28       jackpot = 1 ether;
29       lastInvestmentTimestamp = 0;
30    }
31 }
```

Figure 4.12. The GovernMental smart contract.

An investor who is also a miner could actively exclude transactions of other investors aiming for exceeding the time limit of one minute. More importantly, a successful miner provides the timestamp of when the block was mined. Thus, an investor-miner who mines a block could time-forward the block timestamp to receive the jackpot.

A comprehensive summary of all vulnerabilities in GovernMental can be found in [76].

4.7 DENIAL-OF-SERVICE: EXCEEDING BLOCK GAS LIMIT

Besides the gas limit for individual transactions, Ethereum also has a block gas limit. This is the gas limit for the entire block, and is set by miners. Transactions cannot exceed the block gas limit or they will fail. This can be exploited to create a Denial of Service attack.

There are cases when a smart contract needs to issue ether payments to multiple Ethereum accounts. One example is refunding the excess ether

```
1   function refundRemainingBalances() external onlyOwner {
2     for (uint i = 0; i < participants.length; i++) {
3       address participant = participants[i];
4       uint256 remainingBalance = balances[participant];
5       if (remainingBalance > 0) {
6         balances[participant] = 0;
7         participant.transfer(remainingBalance);
8         emit RefundIssued(participant, remainingBalance);
9       }
10    }
11  }
```

Figure 4.13. A method that can cause a denial of service when the array grows too long.

to token sale participants once all tokens are distributed. Consider the flawed implementation of this functionality as shown in Figure 4.13.

The method iterates over an array of contributors (participants in this case) and checks the remaining balance for each of them. If the balance is above zero, the method issues refunds using transfer(). The mechanism looks straightforward, however, it has a significant issue.

If the array grows too large, calling the method leads to exceeding the Ethereum block gas limit. In the contract code shown earlier, the amount of gas required to send a refundRemainingBalances() transaction is proportional to the length of the participants array. Issuing refunds to 1,000 contributors costs more than a million of gas: in our quick experiment, it was 1138944. At the time of writing this book, the block gas limit on the Ethereum mainnet is around eight million. With this gas limit, when the number of participants eligible for refunds gets close to 8,000, this limit is exceeded, the call throws the "block gas limit exceeded" exception, and no participants are issued a refund. The owner has to pay all the gas fees associated with the method call, regardless whether it succeeds or not.

While the design of this contract is flawed even without the presence of malicious users, it also creates the potential for a Denial-of-Service (DoS) attack. An attacker can create a new Ethereum address, become a participant in the contract in the quickest and cheapest way possible, and repeat the process until the participants array is long enough to cause the block gas limit exception. When this happens, no participant will be issued a refund.

In some cases, the contract owner may be capable of taking measures for restricting multi-account participation to prevent this kind of exploit, but generally speaking, associating real-world entities to Ethereum addresses is a hard problem. Many blockchain applications do not have a good mechanism for handling this, and such a mechanism may be costly to implement and maintain.

```
1   function refundRemainingBalancesAsBatch(
2     uint startIndex,
3     uint endIndex
4   ) external onlyOwner {
5     uint _endIndex = endIndex;
6     if (_endIndex > participants.length) {
7       _endIndex = participants.length;
8     }
9
10    for (uint i = startIndex; i < _endIndex; i++) {
11      address participant = participants[i];
12      uint256 remainingBalance = balances[participant];
13      if (remainingBalance > 0) {
14        balances[participant] = 0;
15        require(participant.send(remainingBalance));
16        emit RefundIssued(participant, remainingBalance);
17      }
18    }
19  }
```

Figure 4.14. Splitting the iteration into batches for the iteration not to exceed the gas limit.

In addition to the DoS attack, malicious users may cause some harm by making it more expensive for the contract owner to operate the contract. This is a high risk for contracts issuing recurring payments.

Figure 4.14 shows an example where the smart contract developer is aware of the block gas limit issue so instead of delivering all the refunds at once, he creates a contract where the balances are delivered in batches instead. The owner can control batch sizes and offsets using two newly added parameters: startIndex and endIndex. The number of participants who receive a refund as a part of the same transaction is now controlled by the contract owner.

While the batching approach helps with preventing the DoS attack described in this section, it is still flawed and suboptimal. First, this approach does not prevent all types of DoS attacks: such as Section 4.8 for an example. Next, the contract owner still has to pay all gas fees associated with a transaction, which can be expensive. And finally, the smart contract owner becomes responsible for keeping track of the batches, which adds more maintenance complexity.

The recommended approach to designing refund functionality is designing it so that the participants are required to issue a transaction to claim a refund. An example is shown in the next section.

4.8 DENIAL-OF-SERVICE: TRANSACTION REVERT

Consider the case when an adversarial participant, instead of using a regular account, creates a proxy contract for becoming a participant in the

```
1   contract Adversary {
2     function() {
3       revert();
4     }
5   }
```

Figure 4.15. Denial-of-Service by a transaction revert.

```
1   function claimRefund() external {
2     uint256 remainingBalance = balances[msg.sender];
3     if (remainingBalance > 0) {
4       balances[msg.sender] = 0;
5       msg.sender.transfer(remainingBalance);
6       emit RefundIssued(msg.sender, remainingBalance);
7     }
8   }
```

Figure 4.16. Design pattern for issuing refunds in a way that prevents DoS attacks.

refund contract example of Section 4.7. The contract's fallback function has only one operation: `revert()`. See Figure 4.15.

This implementation allows for another type of DoS attack. As noted in Section 4.4, sending ether to a contract invokes the contract's fallback function. In the earlier example, the contract issues the `revert` EVM instruction whenever it receives ether. This causes the transaction to revert, causing all other ether transfers made as a part of the same transaction to revert as well. Consequently, any users that happen to be in the same batch as the malicious user do not receive the refund.

The issue can be resolved by using the withdraw design pattern [70] shown in Figure 4.16. Instead of sending refunds to users as in the previous example, this design has users claim their refunds individually like a withdrawal.

This not only prevents DoS attacks through the transaction revert approach, but also prevents the block gas limit attack because a failure to issue a refund to the caller (`msg.sender`) no longer affects the ability to issue refunds to other users. In addition, it leads to gas savings and reduced operational complexity for the contract owner, because the owner no longer needs to send the expensive `refundRemainingBalances()` transaction or keep track of the refund batches.

4.9 ATTEMPTS TO GENERATE RANDOM NUMBERS

Generating random numbers is difficult for deterministic systems like Ethereum, so pseudo-random number generation is usually used instead.

Since Ethereum and Solidity do not provide primitives for this, developers attempt to generate their own pseudo-random numbers, usually using some data from the blockchain, but this approach can be exploited.

4.9.1 MECHANISM

A popular application of smart contracts is lotteries, raffles and casino-type games. Such games usually require generating random numbers. However, smart contract computations on Ethereum require deterministic results when executed by all the miners independently.

The global state of Ethereum is maintained through a decentralized consensus on what computations should have been performed and what the inputs for those computations were. If there was an option for the nodes to generate random numbers, it would be impossible to achieve consensus on a global state. Therefore, all computations on Ethereum must be deterministic and Ethereum cannot provide primitives for generating random numbers.

The developers often attempt to overcome the absence of such primitives by using information related to the state of the blockchain [87]. This is most often the current block hash obtained by calling `blockhash (block.number)`. Sometimes, the developers also use the time when the block was mined (built-in `block.timestamp`), or they use this information as a seed for some algorithm that is to generate a random number.

Such practices build on the common assumption that contract methods are called by humans only. However, this is false as smart contract methods can be called by other smart contracts. Because those contracts share the same state of the blockchain, they can replicate the computation and generate all the random numbers before actually making the call. Based on the generated value, they can decide whether it is beneficial to make such a call or not.

4.9.2 EXAMPLE

Consider the contract in Figure 4.17 that allows two players to enter in a game, each with 1 ether. Once this happens, the first player to enter is expected to call a method for rewarding the winner. The winner is selected based on the current block hash: the first player wins if the block hash is even, otherwise the other player wins. The winner receives the entire balance.

The first player can implement a proxy contract (see Figure 4.18) that allows both signing up as a player, as well as calling the `rewardWinner()` method. Furthermore, before calling the `rewardWinner()` method, the

```
1   contract EvenGame {
2
3     address public player1;
4     address public player2;
5
6     // Allows the players to enter the game if they transfer 1 eth
7     function enter() public payable {
8       require(msg.value == 1 ether);
9       if (player1 == 0x0) {
10        player1 = msg.sender;
11      } else if (player2 == 0x0) {
12        player2 = msg.sender;
13      } else {
14        revert();
15      }
16    }
17
18    // Rewards player1 if the block hash is even, otherwise rewards
19    // player2. Then starts a new game.
20    function rewardWinner() public {
21      require(msg.sender == player1);
22      require(player1 != 0x0);
23      require(player2 != 0x0);
24
25      uint256 winner = uint256(blockhash(block.number)) % 2;
26      if (winner == 0) {
27        // player1 won
28        player1.transfer(address(this).balance);
29      } else {
30        player2.transfer(address(this).balance);
31      }
32
33      player1 = 0x0;
34      player2 = 0x0;
35    }
36 }
```

Figure 4.17. A game contract that attempts to use randomness to determine a winner.

contract can check the block hash, who the winner will be, and whether it is beneficial to call the method now, or leave it for a later occasion.

This exploit was recently found in the Fomo3D game which promised random airdrops to users who participated in the game [84]. Fomo3D used multiple pieces of information to generate the random number, but failed on the same core principle. We will talk more about Fomo3D in Section 4.10.1.

4.9.3 PREVENTION

As of now, there is no correct approach for generating randomness on-chain. Some sources recommend taking into account cross-chain information such as the state of the Bitcoin chain [78], however, this is by no means easy to do.

```
1   contact EvenGame {
2     function enter() public payable;
3     function rewardWinner(address player1, address player2) public;
4   }
5
6   contract EvenGameProxy {
7
8     // Proxy call to enter the game
9     function enter(address gameContract) public payable {
10      EvenGame(gameContract).enter.value(msg.value)();
11    }
12
13    // Proxy call that calls only in the favourable case.
14    function letMeWin(address gameContract) public {
15      uint256 winner = uint256(blockhash(block.number)) % 2;
16      if (winner == 0) {
17        // make the winner call
18        EvenGame(gameContract).rewardWinner();
19      } else {
20        // this block hash does not make us win
21        revert();
22      }
23    }
24
25    // Allows accepting ether.
26    function() public payable {
27    }
28  }
```

Figure 4.18. A proxy contract that can enter EvenGame from Figure 4.17 and always wins.

Another alternative in the case of our EvenGame example or similar lotteries is recording the user's decision before the winner can be determined. In this case the winner may be based on data from some future state of the chain.

Using this approach, which is illustrated in Figure 4.19, the EvenGame would force player1 to resolve the game, then wait a certain number of blocks. Once this number of blocks elapsed, the player would call the method again to resolve the game. The technique is also described in [78, 86, 87].

To exploit a contract designed in this manner, player1 would have to be able to predict the parity of the block hash many blocks ahead. Beyond a nominal number of blocks, this is not feasible with current computational means.

4.10 ENSURING CONTRACTS ARE CALLED BY HUMANS

Many smart contract vulnerabilities stem from the fact that smart contract methods can be called by other smart contracts. Hence, developers often

```
1   contract EvenGame {
2
3     address public player1;
4     address public player2;
5     uint256 public frozenAt;
6
7     // Allows the players enter the game if they transfer 1 ether
8     function enter() public payable {
9       require(msg.value == 1 ether);
10      if (player1 == 0x0) {
11        player1 = msg.sender;
12      } else if (player2 == 0x0) {
13        player2 = msg.sender;
14      } else {
15        revert();
16      }
17    }
18
19    // Freezes the game and records the commitment of player1 to
         resolve
20    // the game 25 blocks later.
21    function freezeState() public {
22      require(msg.sender = player1);
23      require(player1 != 0x0);
24      require(player2 != 0x0);
25
26      frozenAt = block.number;
27    }
28
29    // Rewards player1 if the block hash is even, otherwise rewards
30    // player2. Then starts a new game.
31    function rewardWinner() public {
32      // this can now be open to both the players
33      // require(msg.sender == player1);
34      require(player1 != 0x0);
35      require(player2 != 0x0);
36      require(frozenAt != 0);
37      require(block.number - 25 > frozenAt);
38
39      blockNumber = frozenAt + 25;
40      uint256 winner = uint256(blockhash(blockNumber)) % 2;
41      if (winner == 0) {
42        // player1 won
43        player1.transfer(address(this).balance);
44      } else {
45        player2.transfer(address(this).balance);
46      }
47
48      player1 = 0x0;
49      player2 = 0x0;
50      frozenAt = 0;
51    }
52  }
```

Figure 4.19. A version of EvenGame which mitigates random number generation exploits.

attempt to restrict methods so they can only be called by humans. These attempts are sometimes flawed.

4.10.1 MECHANISM

One common method of attempting to make sure contracts are only called by humans is to check that the size of code associated with an Ethereum address is 0, using the assembly function `extcodesize()`. Figure 4.20 illustrates this approach. Unfortunately, this approach is flawed. A proxy smart contract can make a call to another smart contract at any point of its life cycle. In particular, it can make such a call inside of its constructor as shown in Figure 4.21.

During the execution of the constructor, the blockchain still does not contain the code for the smart contract being created. This will be the case after the execution of the constructor is complete, but not before. There-fore, the `extcodesize(msg.sender)` in the target contract returns 0 when invoked from a smart contract constructor.

4.10.2 PREVENTION

The best way of ensuring that methods are called by users is using

$$require(msg.sender == tx.origin)$$

```
1   // this does not work!
2   modifier isHuman() {
3      address _addr = msg.sender;
4      uint256 _codeLength;
5
6      assembly {_codeLength := extcodesize(_addr)}
7      require(_codeLength == 0, "No smart contracts!");
8      _;
9   }
```

Figure 4.20. A modifier that attempts checking if the sender is a smart contract, but does not always work.

```
1   contract CallInConstructor {
2
3      constructor(address target) public {
4         // make a call here
5         target.call(...);
6      }
7   }
```

Figure 4.21. Penetrating the modifier shown in Figure 4.20.

```
1  modifier isHuman() {
2    require(msg.sender == tx.origin, "No smart contracts!");
3    _;
4  }
```

Figure 4.22. This modifier prevents smart contracts from making calls to the method.

This assertion checks that the account that initiated the transaction is the sender of the message that triggered the method. This is never the case when a proxy smart contract is used, not even when the call is made from the constructor.

While this construction restricts the callers to externally owned accounts only, it must be noted that it should be used only when absolutely necessary and not as a security measure. The primary goal of implementing secure smart contracts is that the logic and individual methods are safe regardless of who the caller is.

Furthermore, preventing methods from being called by other smart contracts decreases the usability of your smart contract in automated systems, and effectively restricts users. For example, since Ethereum does not have native support for multi-signature accounts, any multi-signature wallet needs to be implemented as a smart contract. By prohibiting calls by external smart contracts, one effectively prohibits calls from multi-signature wallets (and all other similar smart contract-based dApps).

4.10.3 REAL-WORLD EXAMPLE: FOMO3D PONZI SCHEME

Fomo3D [88] is a Ponzi scheme smart contract which runs in rounds and encourages participants to purchase "keys" (somewhat equivalent to lottery tickets) with ether in hopes of winning a lottery. The last person to purchase a key within the round wins the jackpot. Every time a participant purchases a key, the duration of the current round is extended.

> This smart contract exhibited a number of vulnerabilities, including attempts at random number generation, and attempts at limiting contract calls to humans.

The Fomo3D smart contract[1] was published on Ethereum on July 6, 2018 and quickly gained popularity. When its balance exceeded 17,000 ETH, the Ethereum community became interested in the potential impact

---

[1] Contract address 0xa62142888aba8370742be823c1782d17a0389da1

Fomo3D would have on the Ethereum ecosystem and formulated some predictions about its eventual outcome. The most viable prediction was that Fomo3D would keep accumulating ether until the balance became so large that mining pools would eventually collude in an effort to win the game [85]. Another notable prediction was that the game had the potential to destroy the Ethereum network by consuming all (or at least a great majority of) ether in existence and transferring that ether to a single user [83]. None of the aforementioned happened though. The game was won through an elaborate attack on the Ethereum mainnet on August 22, 2018, yielding the winner 10,469.66 ETH.

There are some notable events that took place during the first round of Fomo3D that are interesting from a smart contract security perspective. First, in order to encourage participants to purchase keys, after every purchase of a key, the smart contract transfers 1 percent of incoming ether into a pool dedicated to airdrops. With every purchase over 0.1 ETH, the smart contract "randomly" assesses whether the purchaser is eligible for an airdrop from this pool. Unfortunately, the "randomness" is not very random. Rather than generating a true random number, the smart contract performed a deterministic computation based on several seeds taken from the current state of the blockchain.

From Section 4.9, we know it is impossible to generate truly random numbers on Ethereum. The existence of random numbers would contradict the fundamental principles of the network. Therefore, all computations on Ethereum must be deterministic and randomness as a feature cannot exist.

Due to this limitation, the authors of Fomo3D decided to derive "randomness" from the current state of the blockchain by performing computations on *block.timestamp, block.difficulty, block.coinbase, block.gaslimit*, the timestamp of the block, the block number and *msg.sender*. Some of these values are hard to predict when a user submits a transaction to the network (because the user does not know in which block the transaction will be mined), but they are all known at the moment when the transaction computations are being carried out. This means that if the user creates a proxy smart contract, it can first evaluate all these seeds, replicate the deterministic computations that produce the "randomness," and based on the outcome decide whether it should make an external call and trigger a transaction. This was noticed for example in [84]. The technique is demonstrated in smart contracts in Figures 4.17 and 4.18.

In order to prevent this possible exploit, the developers of Fomo3D decided to prohibit purchases that do not come directly from an externally owned account (that is, not a smart contract). For this purpose, they used the EVM assembly instruction `extcodesize(_address)` that returns the size of code associated with an Ethereum address. They assumed that code size of a smart contract is never 0, but as explained in Section 4.10, this assumption is not valid through the entire lifecycle of a smart contract. Specifically, if `extcodesize(_address)` is invoked from the constructor of the contract on address `_address`, it returns 0.

This is all an attacker needs to attack the airdrop feature of Fomo3D. By implementing a smart contract that, inside of its constructor, checks that the seeds yield the desired "random" outcome, a smart contract can be programmed to only purchase keys when airdrops are guaranteed. If the airdrop value exceeds the cost of purchasing a key, the whole purchase results in a positive amount of ether arriving to the attacker's account.

As described in Section 4.10 and Figure 4.22, the way to prevent a method from being called by another contracts is `require(msg.sender == tx.origin)`, but there may have been an even better approach to secure the contract. The proper way of implementing the airdrop feature in Fomo3D would be using the approach of committing user decisions at a certain block and then resolving the results at a later block as described in Section 4.9 (also noted in [86]).

The second interesting event around Fomo3D happened at the end of the first round. Despite the general assumption that the game would be won by a colluding mining pool [85], the round ended due to a different attack. The first round of Fomo3D was won by a user[2] through a proxy smart contract[3] that performed a systematic attack that exploited the profit seeking behavior of the Ethereum miners.

When a user broadcasts an Ethereum transaction, it becomes part of the mempool of transactions. The miners then select transactions from the mempool, organize them into a block and then attach the block to the blockchain via proof-of-work. The key point to notice here is that the selection of transactions that will be placed in the next block is left to the discretion of the miners. Because miners are motivated by profit, transactions that are valuable, that is, those that consume a lot of gas and whose sender specified the highest gas price, will get packed into blocks before other transactions do. Furthermore, the size of blocks in terms of the maximum amount of gas per block is limited (currently 8,000,000). Therefore, by submitting many transactions that nearly consume an entire block and that yield gas revenue for the miners exceeding the yield of

---

[2] Address 0xa169df5ed3363cfc4c92ac96c6c5f2a42fccbf85
[3] Address 0xa62142888aba8370742be823c1782d17a0389da1

other transactions on the network, the attacker was able to prevent other transactions from getting mined.

The attacker purchased a key in block 6191896 and then intentionally congested the network between blocks 6191898 and 6191906, which was sufficient for the time limit for the next key purchase to elapse. During the attack, the number of transactions per block decreased from around 100 to less than 10. Detailed analysis is available in [85].

The possibility of manipulating transactions in this fashion was well documented before Fomo3D; however, it was always cited as a potential attack from the side of the miners [77, 81]. The Ethereum community was also warned that colluding miners could actively exclude transactions from other participants from blocks in an effort to cheat and win the game themselves [81]. However, the end of round 1 of Fomo3D was the first time an external user took advantage of the profit-seeking and predictable algorithm for selecting transactions to be mined. Moreover, all they required for this attack was some ether to cover the high gas cost. This is an important lesson for all applications that rely on security mechanisms that require users to submit transactions.

4.11   ZERO INITIAL BALANCE ASSUMPTION

Consider the excerpt of a token sale contract's fallback function shown in Figure 4.23. Unless the sale is active, the transaction is immediately reverted, and ether contribution is rejected. Otherwise, amountRaised is increased by the contribution amount (msg.value). Then there is an assert() which checks that contract balance is no higher than the contribution amount(amountRaised), otherwise an exception is thrown.

The smart contract owner mistakenly assumes that the contract balance will always be equal to or lower than the contribution amount. They assume that the contract balance will equal the contribution amount unless the owner withdraws some money after the sale starts, making the balance become lower than the amount raised.

```
1  function() public payable {
2      require(saleIsActive);
3      amountRaised = amountRaised.add(msg.value);
4      require(amountRaised >= this.balance);
5      ... // other actions
6  }
```

Figure 4.23. An excerpt from a token sale contract mistakenly assuming balance of the contract.

However, there is a situation when this is not the case. The selfdestruct EVM call does not trigger the contract's fallback function (as noted in [71]). Before the sale starts, an attacker forcibly moves some ether to the current contract by destroying another contract and specifying the current one as a beneficiary. For the sake of the example, assume the destroyed contract's balance is 15 Ether, so the amount forcibly moved to the current contract is also 15 Ether.

After the sale starts, a regular user contributes 10 ether to the contract. In this case, amountRaised is 10 ether and this.balance is 10 + 15 = 25 ether. Therefore, the assertion amountRaised >= this.balance is violated, and the contribution is unexpectedly rejected. This makes the sale contract partially unusable, as nobody can contribute an amount that is lower than the initial, forcibly moved, balance.

A similar effect is achieved by using the contract address as a beneficiary for mining. This, however, is harder to achieve, because the miner has to exert more effort and succeed in mining a block.

Smart contracts should never rely on the zero initial balance assumption. There is no way to prevent ether being sent to an Ethereum account.

4.12   DEPRECATED CALL STACK DEPTH ATTACK

The Call Stack Depth Attack is an exploit of the hard limit of 1024 for Ethereum's call stack. This vulnerability was fixed by EIP150 [72] but is presented here for educational and informative purposes.

Consider the code example in Figure 4.24. The buyItem method allows a user to buy an item from the present owner by sending ether matching or exceeding the item price. The present owner becomes lastOwner and receives the full amount of ether sent by the new owner.

Before the EIP 150 hardfork was in place, the code in Figure 4.24 was vulnerable to the call stack depth attack. An attacker creates a smart contract that buys an item on their behalf. The attacker's smart contract method is designed to recursively call itself 1023 times before calling the buyItem

```
1   function buyItem(address item) external payable {
2     if (owner[item] != msg.sender && price[item] <= msg.value) {
3       address lastOwner = owner[item];
4       owner[item] = msg.sender;
5       lastOwner.send(msg.value);
6     }
7   }
```

Figure 4.24. Code prone to the deprecated call stack depth attack.

method. When the method is invoked, the method `send` does not succeed and returns `false`, because the call stack limit is exceeded (1024). However, there is no check for the return value around after `send` call, therefore, ownership of the `buyItem` item goes through. As a result, `lastOwner` no longer possesses the item, and unexpectedly gets nothing in return.

The EIP 150 hardfork introduces changes to the gas logic, reducing the maximum allowed amount of gas as the call stack gets deeper. The child (nested) recursion calls are not allowed to consume more than roughly 63/64 of the gas of the parent call. Therefore, a transaction running a call stack depth attack will trigger an "out of gas" exception long before it reaches the 1024 limit. The maximum call stack size that is currently possible is around 340.

4.13 LIBRARY DESIGN FLAWS

Some Ethereum contracts implement functionality that can be reused in other contracts. Examples include on-chain data structures, token contract interfaces, multi-signature wallets, and others. Such contracts, or *libraries*, are often deployed to the blockchain once and then referenced multiple times by other smart contracts requiring this functionality, or *client* contracts.

A client contract interacts with a library using the `delegatecall()` method. When using `delegatecall()`, the library code is executed in the context of the calling client contract. This means any data that is accessed or stored during such execution is located in the storage space of the client, not the library.

While libraries provide a clear benefit of encapsulating shared functionality, there is an important security consideration. If a library has a security vulnerability, all instances of the client contract using that library are at risk. The immutable nature of smart contracts on Ethereum exacerbates the issue: if a vulnerability is detected or exploited, there is no way to "patch" the library by re-deploying it to the same address. In addition, many client contracts do not have a way of switching from one library version to another, making them hard-wired to the flawed library version.

Two commonly known examples of library exploits are the Parity multi-signature wallet hacks [20, 73]. Both hacks happened in 2017, in July and November, respectively.

The first example involved a vulnerability in the wallet library allowing unexpected wallet ownership transfer. This vulnerability was exploited on July 19, 2017 when unknown parties managed to get owner access to wallet contracts and move funds from the wallets [73]. The example library in Figure 4.25 illustrates the vulnerability.

```
1   contract WalletLibrary {
2     address private _owner;
3     event MoneyMoved(
4       address beneficiary
5     );
6
7     function initWallet(address owner) public {
8       _owner = owner;
9     }
10    function moveMoney(address beneficiary) public {
11      // other actions
12      emit MoneyMoved(beneficiary);
13    }
14
15    /// other library methods
16  }
17
18  contract Wallet {
19    WalletLibrary private _walletLibrary;
20    event Deposit(
21      address sender,
22      uint value
23    );
24
25    function Wallet(address walletLibraryAddress) {
26      _walletLibrary = WalletLibrary(walletLibraryAddress);
27      _walletLibrary.initWallet(msg.sender);
28    }
29
30    function() payable {
31      // just being sent some cash?
32      if (msg.value > 0)
33        emit Deposit(msg.sender, msg.value);
34      else if (msg.data.length > 0)
35        _walletLibrary.delegatecall(msg.data);
36    }
37  }
```

Figure 4.25. A library allowing unexpected wallet ownership transfer.

WalletLibrary provides the moveMoney() and initWallet()
methods. An actual wallet—a client for WalletLibrary—is created by
deploying an instance of the Wallet contract. The client wallet is "thin:"
it does not contain much logic and delegates calls to the library contract
for complex wallet operations, such as moveMoney().

In this example, the Wallet's fallback function implements a "super-
class call" mechanism. Any calls made to the methods that are not defined
in the Wallet contract are forwarded to the library contract. For instance,
a user calls moveMoney() on the instance of the Wallet contract. The
Wallet contract does not have the moveMoney() method defined. Therefore, the "catch-all" fallback function executes and does delegatecall()
on the wallet library. msg.data is passed as a parameter: it contains the
method name—moveMoney() and any arguments passed to it. The call is
then processed by the library contract almost as if this was sent directly to it.

The attacker was able to exploit this mechanism in the following way. The attacker creates a transaction `initWallet()` with the attacker's address and sends it to the wallet contract. The wallet contract does not contain the definition of `initWallet()` method. There is no ether sent with the transaction, so `msg.value` is 0, and the branch `msg.value > 0` is skipped. The execution proceeds with the check `msg.data.length > 0` which is true in this case: `msg.data` contains the `initWallet()` method name. Next, the contract does `delegatecall()` on the wallet library instance, which effectively tries to call `initWallet()` on the `WalletLibrary` contract. The wallet library does contain the definition of `initWallet()` method, and this method is executed. Since there is no condition ensuring lack of prior initializations, the method successfully executes and sets the owner to the attacker's address. As noted earlier, `delegatecall()` executes library code in the client contract's context, therefore, the owner is set not for the library, but for the client contract.

On July 20, 2017, a new version of the library contract was deployed that addresses the issue. The essence of the update is captured in the example shown in Figure 4.26.

The added `onlyUninitialized()` modifier prevents re-initialization of the wallet. This makes the repeated `initWallet()` no longer possible.

The updated library, however, remained a regular Solidity contract. When interfaced using the `delegatecall()` operation, the contract

```
1  contract WalletLibrary {
2    address private _owner;
3    event MoneyMoved(
4      address beneficiary
5    );
6
7    bool private isInitialized;
8
9    modifier onlyUninitialized() {
10     require(!isInitialized);
11     _;
12   }
13
14   function initWallet(address owner) public onlyUninitialized {
15     _owner = owner;
16   }
17
18   function moveMoney(address beneficiary) public {
19     emit MoneyMoved(beneficiary);
20   }
21
22   // other library methods
23 }
```

Figure 4.26. A simplified update of the parity contract.

shown earlier acts as a library and uses the client contract's context and storage space. In contrast, when interfaced directly, the contract acts as just a regular contract with its own owner and storage.

This fact was exploited on November 6, 2017 [20]. After the updated library was deployed, it remained in the uninitialized state. The latter did not prevent the wallets from working, because the library was interfaced using `delegatecall()`, which uses the client's context, and the client was initialized. In other words, `isInitialized()` was true for individual client contracts but `false` for the library. So, it was possible to initialize the library and set its owner.

First, the attacker initializes the library by calling `initWallet()` on the library [74]. The method allows for setting the owners for the contract, and the attacker becomes the sole owner of the library. Notably, it is not possible to take ownership back from the attacker, because the new modifier prevents ownership transfer after initialization took place.

Next, the attacker calls the method `kill()` that destroys the contract using the `SUICIDE` EVM instruction. There is no access control violation, because the method is only accessible to the owners, and the attacker was, in fact, the owner.

Since the library no longer exists, any delegate call to the library methods no longer works. This includes the `moveMoney()` method to transfer the money out of the contract. So, the money that stayed in the wallets that reference the exploited library is "frozen."

4.13.1 PREVENTION

The exploit was possible, in part, due to the library being stateful. A better practice is to design libraries to be stateless. There is no need for a library to have its own state, because whenever a library is called using `delegatecall()`, the client's state will be changed, not the library's. Solidity supports the `library` keyword which is more suited for creating libraries [75].

4.14 EXCEPTION HANDLING

King of the Ether Throne [80] was a Ponzi scheme dApp that ran between February 6, 2016 and February 8, 2016, though the contract is still available on the blockchain. A simplified version of the contract is shown in Figure 4.27 (complete source code can be found online [82]). The principle of the scheme was the following. A user can pay a certain

```
1   contract KingOfEtherThrone {
2     address public king;
3     uint public claimPrice = 100;
4     address owner;
5
6     constructor() public {
7       owner = msg.sender;
8       king = msg.sender;
9     }
10
11    function sweepCommission(unit amount) {
12      owner.send(amount);
13    }
14
15    function() public payable {
16      require (msg.value >= claimPrice);
17
18      uint compensation = calculateCompensation();
19      king.send(compensation);
20      king = msg.sender;
21      claimPrice = calculateNewPrice();
22    }
23
24    /* other functions follow */
25  }
26
```

Figure 4.27. A simplified update of the King of the Ether Throne smart contract based on [81].

amount of ether to become the King of Ether. If another user pays more ether, they can assume the throne and become the new king. Some of this ether will then be paid out as compensation to the king that is being replaced.

Recall that there are three ways of transferring ether in Solidity, as described in Section 4.4 (Table 4.1). The developer of the King of the Ether Throne contract used send() to transfer the funds to the departing king (line 19 in Figure 4.27). This method receives a small stipend of 2,300 wei as the gas limit. This gas limit is only sufficient for emitting an event and cannot execute any other code. Furthermore, if the transfer fails, then the function returns false but does not revert the state.

When the contract attempted to compensate the previous king on the contract-based wallet, it would inadvertently execute their fallback function. If the function contained any code beyond emitting an event, the transfer would fail because the gas stipend passed to the call was too low. Since send() fails internally by returning false and does not revert the entire execution, and since the contract does not check the return value, the new king can assume the throne without compensating the old king.

This results in a higher contract balance that the contract owner can sweep in the form of a commission.

There are multiple ways of implementing this contract properly. In order to ensure proper execution of the fallback function, a method `call` with a sufficiently high gas limit (passing all the gas available to this call would be safest) should be used. Then it would be up to the user to provide a sufficiently high gas limit. Second, the contract would need to check the return value of the call and actively call `revert` or `throw` if the call returned `false`.

However, even these precautions would not make the contract completely safe. The new king could implement a transaction revert in their fallback function as shown in Figure 4.15 in Section 4.8.

Due to the active revert, an attempt to transfer ether to such a king would always fail and revert the state. This would result in a DoS attack on the contract as the king could never be replaced.

The proper way of implementing a smart contract for King of the Ether Throne is using a withdrawal design pattern [70] similar to the refund claim method illustrated in Figure 4.16. The contract should internally record the commissions that former kings are eligible for, and expose a method for them to claim those commissions.

When the issues were reported, King of the Ether Throne's operator published an announcement on their website. They conducted an investigation that resulted in refunding ether to those who were eligible, and published a detailed postmortem report on the contract [3].

4.15 VALIDATED ARGUMENTS AND THE ETHEREUM SHORT ADDRESS ATTACK

The method calls in transactions are part of the *data* field [65, 79]. This field contains a serialized hexadecimal representation of the method signature and the arguments. The first four bytes are the first four bytes of the Keccak256 hash of the signature (sometimes also referred to as the *prototype*) of the method. The rest are concatenated representations of arguments as defined by the ABI specification [79].

Each argument is represented by a string of bits encoded in hexadecimal form. Numbers and addresses are represented as big-endian 256 bits with all the leading zeroes included.

For example, in a call to a method

```
withdraw(address a, uint256 n)
```

with arguments

```
a = 0x74814602062af64fd7a83155645ddb265598220e

n = 1,
```

the representation of the arguments would consist of the bit-wise concatenation of

```
0000 0000 0000 0000 0000 0000 0000 0000
0000 0000 0000 0000 0000 0000 0000 0000
0000 0000 0000 0000 0000 0000 0000 0000
0111 0100 1000 0001 0100 0110 0000 0010
0000 0110 0010 1010 1111 0110 0100 1111
1101 0111 1010 1000 0011 0001 0101 0101
0110 0100 0101 1101 1101 1011 0010 0110
0101 0101 1001 1000 0010 0010 0000 1110
```

with

```
0000 0000 0000 0000 0000 0000 0000 0000
0000 0000 0000 0000 0000 0000 0000 0000
0000 0000 0000 0000 0000 0000 0000 0000
0000 0000 0000 0000 0000 0000 0000 0000
0000 0000 0000 0000 0000 0000 0000 0000
0000 0000 0000 0000 0000 0000 0000 0000
0000 0000 0000 0000 0000 0000 0000 0000
0000 0000 0000 0000 0000 0000 0000 0001
```

If a user does not provide the required number of bits, this bit string is padded with zeros on the right side. Consider again the aforementioned method withdraw that accepts an Ethereum address and a number of tokens in this order. If the address ends with some zeros, for example:

```
a = 0x74814602062af64fd7a83155645ddb2655982200,
```

its bit representation will be

```
0000 0000 0000 0000 0000 0000 0000 0000
0000 0000 0000 0000 0000 0000 0000 0000
0000 0000 0000 0000 0000 0000 0000 0000
0111 0100 1000 0001 0100 0110 0000 0010
0000 0110 0010 1010 1111 0110 0100 1111
1101 0111 1010 1000 0011 0001 0101 0101
0110 0100 0101 1101 1101 1011 0010 0110
0101 0101 1001 1000 0010 0010 0000 0000
```

If a user submits transaction with the last two zeros missing, that is, with arguments

```
a = 0x74814602062af64fd7a83155645ddb26559822

n = 1
```

the EVM will "borrow" leading bits from n that determines the number of tokens to complete the address. This number n will then be padded with zeros from the right, effectively receiving a bitwise shift left.

The representation that the EVM will interpret is:

```
0000 0000 0000 0000 0000 0000 0000 0000
0000 0000 0000 0000 0000 0000 0000 0000
0000 0000 0000 0000 0000 0000 0000 0000
0111 0100 1000 0001 0100 0110 0000 0010
0000 0110 0010 1010 1111 0110 0100 1111
1101 0111 1010 1000 0011 0001 0101 0101
0110 0100 0101 1101 1101 1011 0010 0110
0101 0101 1001 1000 0010 0010 0000 0000

0000 0000 0000 0000 0000 0000 0000 0000
0000 0000 0000 0000 0000 0000 0000 0000
0000 0000 0000 0000 0000 0000 0000 0000
0000 0000 0000 0000 0000 0000 0000 0000
0000 0000 0000 0000 0000 0000 0000 0000
0000 0000 0000 0000 0000 0000 0000 0000
0000 0000 0000 0000 0000 0000 0000 0000
0000 0000 0000 0000 0000 0001 0000 0000
```

On-chain smart contracts often interact with off-chain systems. For example, a centralized exchange may maintain a ledger of user balances in an off-chain database, and store the ether for those balances on several smart contracts that allow interaction only with the owner—the exchange itself.

When users want to withdraw their funds, they submit a request through the exchange's user interface. The system checks their balance on the off-chain ledger and, if the balance is sufficient, issues a transaction to the smart contract which automatically transfers ether to the provided address.

Imagine what would happen if a user opens an account with such an exchange and provides an address with truncated trailing zeros as the one previously shown. If the user interface of the exchange does not validate the address,[4] the internal ledger can record a non-zero balance for the truncated address. If a user requests a token withdrawal, the check for a sufficient balance passes on to the internal ledger of the exchange, but when arguments are packed into a transaction submitted to Ethereum, the lack of bits in the address will create a bitwise shift effectively increasing the number of tokens being withdrawn. If the exchange smart contract itself does not sanitize the address and verify user balance, it will transfer an incorrect number of tokens.

The Ethereum short address vulnerability was observed [69], but never used in practice. Luckily, the transfer of the tokens failed as the shortening of the Ethereum address resulted in such a large bit shift that it exceeded the balance of the contract, and in fact, the supply of the token itself). Therefore, this attack remains theoretical.

The Ethereum short address vulnerability might appear as a security flaw in off-chain systems. However, the main message here is that smart contracts should never rely on off-chain systems for verification of state such as balance, and should never assume that the method will be called with well-formed data that will properly decode into valid arguments.

---

[4] Ethereum addresses do not support checksums. A checksum based on the capitalization of letters when written as hexadecimal string was added by EIP55, but as capitalization of letters does not matter for conversion to bits, such a checksum is sometimes hard to enforce.

CHAPTER 5

WRITING SECURE SMART CONTRACTS

As the previous chapters suggest, there are many, often subtle, issues that may arise when engineering a smart contract. Using insecure coding patterns such as writing to state variables after calling another contract can lead to re-entrancy attacks. Or, there may be deeper game theoretic design flaws, such as inadvertent centralization. So how can developers avoid such pitfalls while writing smart contracts?

While this process may be intimidating at first, there are numerous resources available to help prevent these issues. Academic papers and blog posts often describe newly found vulnerabilities, design patterns, and best practices for smart contract development. Smart contract analyzers can automatically check for a number of common security flaws. Various tools can aid in developing robust test suites for your smart contracts. Or, smart contract security experts can manually audit smart contracts to further ensure correctness. In this chapter, we'll go through some of these resources, along with some best practices for developing secure smart contracts. While there is no "one right way" to develop a smart contract, we believe that the following guidelines outline an effective approach to development, which has been followed numerous times by the authors of this book.

5.1 ENGINEERING PROCESSES AND STANDARDS

Following proper standards acts as a first line of defense for avoiding security issues. Although some of these principles are solidity-specific, many are more general and can be applied to any project. Given the amount at stake when deploying smart contracts, we suggest these as a minimal set of standards for development.

5.1.1 GENERAL PROJECT STRUCTURE

Most solidity-based projects are developed in a framework called `truffle` [89], which facilitates code compilation, deployment to blockchains (both for test networks and mainnet), and testing. `truffle` interacts well with other tools in the domain, such as local test networks such as `ganache` [91]. These test networks allow developers to locally deploy contracts and run tests. Other tools such as `solidity-coverage` [93] can automatically assess the coverage metrics associated with a `truffle` test suite, as discussed further in Section 5.2. Additionally, other well-vetted code repositories such as `Open-Zeppelin-Solidity` [92]—a repository of many standard smart contracts such as `SafeMath` for protected arithmetic, or various token specifications, can be easily imported into `truffle` projects using the `npm` package manager. It is preferable to import such projects through package managers rather than cloning the files directly into the project; this avoids simple mistakes through making changes to already vetted smart contracts, and generally avoids cluttering the repository with dependencies.

Projects should be developed within a *version control system* such as `git` to facilitate collaboration. In a typical project, different branches are developed to mitigate issues that arise in code that is deployed in a production environment or is deployed to mainnet. Bug fixes or other tasks are developed in separate branches and then merged into the `develop` branch after being vetted by other developers for quality and correctness through pull requests. The `develop` branch serves as the main branch for active development. Certain checks should be considered before merging in new changes:

- Does the new code perform the desired functionality, whether that be fixing a bug or adding a new feature?
- If applicable, have new tests been added to exercise the functionality of the new code?
- Does the code adhere to formatting standards, as can be checked by off-the-shelf linters [90]?
- Is the code sufficiently commented?
- Are there better alternative implementations that could be considered?

If the code meets all requirements, it can be merged into the `develop` branch. Moving beyond that, code in the `master` or `production` branch should be a stable release ready for public use, and deployable to mainnet if applicable. Additional vetting should be considered here, such as manual testing on a public network other than mainnet, such as Ropsten.

Ideally, version control is used in conjunction with an issue tracker such as Jira [114]. This allows teams to easily track progress on issues, tasks, and milestones needed to complete the project. *Continuous integration (CI)* could also be used to automatically assess certain qualities of code commits. This should be used in conjunction with a *regression test suite*, which is a series of tests that are evaluated to any commit before merging it into either the `develop` or `production` branch. CI tools can automatically run test suites on each commit, ensuring that the modified code still passes the suite of regression tests.

5.1.2 DESIGN PATTERNS

In Chapter 4, we introduced some of the most common vulnerabilities to look out for when writing a smart contract. These issues have been distilled into a set of design patterns that are useful for avoiding vulnerabilities [98, 99].

- When making calls to external contracts, ensure all pre-conditions have been checked and state variables have been updated before the call. This helps to mitigate re-entrancy vulnerabilities. Additionally, use a mutex if re-entrancy must be absolutely avoided [100].
- Use `require` statements to validate function inputs and precondition checks, and use `assert` to ensure other invariants always hold. Remember that `assert` uses up all remaining gas in the transaction, whereas `require` refunds all remaining gas.
- Ensure that important functions are pausable (cf. [101]) to mitigate damages in the case of attack.
- Ensure that the result of any `call()` or `send()` invocations of external contract are checked upon return. In most cases, using `transfer()`, which raises an exception when the called function fails is preferred.
- Avoid using timestamps in conditionals involving critical operations such as sending ether, as they can be manipulated by the miner.
- Limit the balance of sensitive smart contracts when possible, such that if a smart contract is attacked, the risk will be mitigated. This could be either through manual transfers of ether to secure wallets, or limitations on transfers to the smart contract if its balance is too high.

- Avoid integer overflow and underflow vulnerabilities through the use of SafeMath functions [102].
- Be explicit with function modifiers, and opt for the most strict modifiers allowable.

Figure 5.1. Recommended design patterns and practices for developing smart contracts. Adopted from [98, 99].

5.1.3 DOCUMENTATION

Proper documentation allows both developers and end-users of the system to better assess the intended functionality and correctness of your smart contract. Even if there are no clear vulnerabilities such as a re-entrancy bug in the code, the semantics of the code may not reflect what is intended by the smart contract writer. In the smart contract domain, documentation typically comes in form of whitepapers, requirements and specification documents, README files, and code-level comments.

Requirements documents specify *what* is needed of the smart contract. These requirements should include both functional and non-functional requirements. Functional requirements specify what the smart contract should do in various scenarios. For example, a functional requirement for an ICO smart contract may state that investors who purchase tokens in the first funding period will receive a 200 percent bonus on their investment. Non-functional requirements dictate other qualities or attributes that are expected of the smart contract. For example, a non-functional requirement could dictate that a smart contract does not allow arbitrary users to change the owner.

Specification documents elaborate on *how* the smart contract (and surrounding infrastructure) will be designed and developed. These may include things like diagrams depicting how other systems such as dApps will interact with the smart contract, information on APIs that will be exposed, or details on how the smart contract will be linked with other smart contracts or libraries.

Whitepapers often include many of the same details as a requirements or specification document, but are often tailored toward a more general audience, and include details that are not relevant to the functionality of the code. Consequently, it is best to have additional technical documentation beyond a whitepaper. Projects should also include README files in the code repository to allow end-users to quickly get up to speed on using your dApp or smart contract. This should also include instructions for developers to further investigate the project, for example, instructions to run the test suite.

At the code level, each contract and function should be commented with their intended functionality, and where appropriate, the meaning of input and output variables. This should be explicit enough that there is no ambiguity in the intended values of variables or in the functionality. For example, suppose a function exists with the signature `function transfer(address recipient, uint256 value)`, which transfers some amount of funds from `msg.sender`. Users and even other dApps that build upon your ABI should be able to discern the intended semantics of `value` without having to read all of the code associated with the function. Based on this signature alone, it is not clear what unit is intended for what value (for example, is it in wei or ether?). Ideally, the variable itself would be named more explicitly, for example, `valueInWei`. Without explicit documentation, one can only guess at the intended semantics of the program.

5.2 TESTING

All of the aforementioned patterns discuss general guidelines that should be followed by most smart contract projects. However, ensuring that your code adheres to all these guidelines does not guarantee that it correctly implements the *intended semantics* of your project. In other words, even if there are no possible attacks as described earlier, that does not mean that the code behaves as intended by the developer and according to the requirements of the project. Additional manual testing is useful to further ensure correctness of the code.

Currently, the most common environment to develop smart contracts is within a `truffle` project [89]. As there is an abundance of online resources for `truffle` development and testing, we do not delve deeper here. An additional tool called `solidity-coverage` is available to assess the code coverage of your test suite [93]. This interacts well with `truffle` and can be used to quickly assess both the line and branch coverage of your test suite.

Consider the code snippet in Figure 5.2. The contract encodes a computational puzzle game, such that if a user submits a correct answer to the puzzle, they will gain a reward. The `owner` and `reward` are stored as state variables, and two other state variables `multiplier` and `locked` are used to encode the logic of the following `guess` function. The `set_owner` function allows the caller to set the owner to themselves, provided it has not already been set. The owner can end the puzzle with the `destroy_puzzle` function, thus sending the reward back to the owner. Finally, the default payable callback function has two main execution paths. If the owner of the contract calls the function and the puzzle has not already been solved, then the owner may update the reward with a new value. Otherwise, any other address may submit an answer, and if it adheres to the arithmetic constraints, the contract will pay out the reward to the sender, and lock the puzzle to declare it solved.

There are two primary types of tests which should be considered. Unit tests are created to exercise individual pieces of source contract (for example, functions). Different inputs and contract states should be considered to properly test the function's full behavior. In our running example in Figure 5.2, in order to exercise the functionality of the `guess` function, we might have tests where `msg.sender` is either the owner or not, where `msg.value` is equal to 1 ether or not, where the answer is a really small or

```
1   contract Puzzle{
2
3       address public owner;
4       uint256 public reward_pool;
5       uint256 public constant multiplier = 32;
6       bool public locked;
7
8       event Nums(uint256 pre, uint256 post);
9
10      function Puzzle() { }
11
12      function set_owner(){
13          if(owner == address(0)){
14              owner = msg.sender;
15          }
16      }
17
18      function destroy_puzzle(){
19          require(owner == msg.sender);
20          selfdestruct(msg.sender);
21      }
22
23      function guess(uint256 answer) payable{
24          if(msg.sender != owner && msg.value == 1 ether){
25              reward_pool += msg.value;
26              uint256 transformed_answer = answer * multiplier;
27              if(locked)
28                  throw;
29              else{
30                  Nums(answer, transformed_answer);
31                  assert(reward == this.balance);
32                  uint256 reward = reward_pool / 2;
33                  if (transformed_answer < answer){
34                      reward_pool -= reward;
35                      msg.sender.call.value(reward)();
36                      locked = true;
37                  }
38              }
39          }
40      }
41  }
```

Figure 5.2. An example contract that allows users to guess a value, rewarding a correct guess with half the acquired stakes.

really large number, and so on. End-to-end tests are meant to exercise the full behavior of an application from "start" to "finish." Suppose we were developing a crowdsale contract that had a given start time, an end time, a funding goal indicating how much ether must be received to declare the crowdsale a success, and a refund phase if the funding goal is not met. An end-to-end test scenario might first ensure that no users could contribute to the crowdsale before the start, followed by a funding period in which there were not enough contributions to reach the funding goal, followed by tests ensuring that all contributors can receive a refund for their contributions.

When evaluating test suites, two common quality measures are line coverage—the percentage of lines of code for which some test case exercises the line, and branch or path coverage—the percentage of branches (for example, if/else paths) that have been tested. It is generally advised to strive for 100 percent line and branch coverage in smart contract test suites, however it is important to note that coverage alone is not a good measure of test suite quality [103]; more carefully thought out tests may be necessary.

5.3 AUTOMATED SMART CONTRACT ANALYSIS WITH SYMBOLIC EXECUTION

With the myriad of potential security issues in smart contracts, it is difficult to ensure that a smart contract is completely correct. Furthermore, even a test suite with very high coverage can still miss crucial vulnerabilities that may render your smart contract worthless. Thankfully, sophisticated analyzers have been developed to automatically detect some of the most common (and catastrophic) vulnerabilities. Here, we'll discuss several approaches to smart contract analysis along with their strengths and weaknesses, and most importantly, how you can use them to create more secure smart contracts. As such, we only focus on analyzers that are publicly available. This is not intended to provide a comprehensive look at how these tools function (which could be a book on its own right), but simply to provide a working knowledge of how the tools operate, and how to best utilize their results.

5.3.1 A PRIMER IN PROGRAM ANALYSIS AND SYMBOLIC EXECUTION

In a nutshell, bug-finding tools, or *analyzers*, look for execution traces that lead to a faulty state of a program. These may be more "generic" bugs, such as assertion statement violations that are triggered by a particular set of input arguments, or domain-specific vulnerabilities, such as the theft of a contract's balance from a sequence of function calls. Different analyzers tend to target different classes of bug types.

A key component of analysis is determining the feasibility of whether there exist some inputs that lead to this faulty state. Consider the `guess` function in Figure 5.2. Suppose we would like to determine whether the `assert` statement on Line 30 can be violated. In order to first reach the line, a transaction's arguments must satisfy the conditional on Line 24, `locked` must still be false in order to avoid the `throw` statement on Line 29, and finally we must actually violate the conditional in the `assert`. Thus, the following constraints must simultaneously be satisfied:

```
msg.sender != owner && msg.value == 1 ether &&
!locked &&reward != this.balance
```

The first three constraints are clearly satisfied as long as some non-owner user sends a transaction with 1 ether before the puzzle is locked. The last constraint requires additional analysis of the `guess` function. If every call to `guess` up to this point had a value of exactly 1 ether, then `reward` should be equal to the total balance of `Puzzle`.[1] However, in the case that a transaction to `guess` occurs with a value not equal to one ether (or zero), since the conditional is embodied by an `if`-statement rather than a `require`, the function will still accept the ether, ignoring the remaining logic of the function. This updates the balance of the contract without updating the corresponding reward. After such a transaction occurs, any future calls to `guess` from a non-owner account with a value of 1 ether will trigger the assertion statement.

In general, these types of logical constraints can be solved by tools called *satisfiability modulo theories (SMT) solvers*. SMT solvers are capable of automatically determining whether logical formulas such as the one shown earlier are *satisfiable*, that is, whether there exists an assignment to the variables that simultaneously satisfy all of the constraints. If so, the solver produces a *model* assigning each of the variables to a concrete value. Otherwise, the solver returns a *proof* that the formula is *unsatisfiable*, that is, it is impossible to assign all variables in a way that

---

[1] Another way in which `Puzzle`'s balance can increase without increasing `reward` is if some other contract self-destructs and transfers its ether balance to the address of `Puzzle`. In general, the logic of a smart contract should never rely on the value of its balance being some specific value for this reason. For simplicity, we will ignore this case for now.

satisfies all constraints. Most constraints that appear in smart contracts, such as those involving boolean variables or integer arithmetic, can be easily encoded into a formula understandable to an SMT solver, and solved for satisfiability. For this reason, SMT solvers form the backbone of many symbolic analyzers. The SMT solver Z3 is the most common solver used in smart contract symbolic analyzers at this time [97].

Symbolic analyzers work by constructing logical formulas as it considers each path through a program. The "symbolic" aspect of these analyzers comes from the fact that encountered variables, whether they be state variables, function parameters, or local variables, are not required to have concrete values when traversing these paths. Logical formulas are built up through assignment statements or conditionals considered along the path. When a conditional statement is encountered, the SMT solver is invoked to determine if it is feasible to assign concrete values to the variables adhering to the constraints along the path. If so, the analyzer continues down the path (for example, to the body of the if-statement), otherwise, the path is pruned and the search is continued elsewhere. If a "statement of interest" is encountered (such as an assertion statement), additional formulas may be checked with the SMT solver, and if the result indicates a vulnerability, it is reported to the user. More complicated logical formulas must be constructed in order to determine if other vulnerabilities, such as re-entrancy attacks, can occur. We discuss some examples in the following sections.

5.3.2 ARCHITECTURE OF A SYMBOLIC ANALYZER

There are now several smart contract analyzers available, such as Oyente [94], Maian [95], and Mythril [96], which check for a variety of vulnerabilities well-known to the community. Figure 5.3 depicts an example analyzer architecture. The devil is of course in the details, but each of the discussed analyzers bears some semblance to this architecture.

Although our examples traverse paths through source code, most analyzers operate at the bytecode level. If a solidity smart contract is given as input, it is first compiled down to EVM bytecode. During this process, a mapping between bytecode operations and source code lines is maintained, such that if a vulnerability is found, the corresponding lines of code can be reported back to the end-user.

As a second piece of input, the analyzer may receive information regarding the *global state* of the blockchain. This may include current assignments to state variables or the code for related smart contracts, if the analyzer supports such inter-contractual analysis. Including information

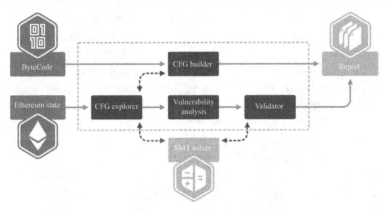

Figure 5.3. An example architecture for a smart contract analyzer.

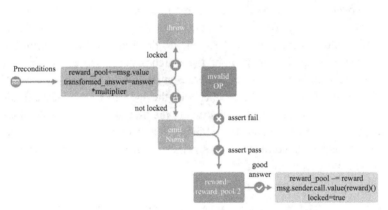

Figure 5.4. The control flow graph of the guess function from Figure 5.2.

about the global state refines the analysis performed by only considering *realistic* settings. If a global state is not given, then the analyzer may simply assign symbolic variables to these variables. This may lead to false positives, since the concrete variables derived from the solver may not reflect reality.

After compilation to bytecode, operations are decomposed into *basic blocks*—sequences of code that must always run together. Consider Lines 25 and 26 of the `guess` function in Figure 5.2, which update the `reward_pool` and instantiate `transformed_answer`. Since there are no conditionals or jumps separating these statements, it is guaranteed that either both lines will be executed, or neither will, so they form a basic block. Consider Figure 5.4. Each box in the diagram constitutes a basic block of the `guess` function. The diagram itself combines basic blocks into a *control flow graph (CFG)*, which connects basic blocks via the conditional statements separating them. This abstraction allows analyzers to more effectively reason about the possible paths through the code, rather than dealing with each operation individually.

Once we obtain the CFG, the analyzer can begin symbolically executing traces of the CFG in search of vulnerabilities (labeled as "Explorer"). This component interacts frequently with the underlying SMT solver to determine the feasibility of traces. An issue here that is common to most symbolic analyzers is known as the *state explosion problem*; as the number of conditionals and jumps increases, the number of possible traces grows exponentially. This makes it infeasible to explore all possible traces; design decisions therefore dictate how the CFG is explored and what limits are imposed on search. For example, configurable parameters may limit the number of jump operations that occur along a given path to some fixed constant, pruning away any traces that exceed the limit. If a loop exists in the code with an unknown upper limit (for example, one that is dependent on some input parameter), then the analyzer may limit the number of times that the loop is symbolically executed. Some paths may be too difficult for the SMT solver to assess feasibility: in this case, timeout limits may prune away difficult traces. The analyzer may also choose to search in a depth-first manner rather than breadth-first, with the hopes of finding "deeper" bugs more quickly. Most analyzers come with reasonable default values for these limits; however, they are often configurable, and this may have a significant impact on the types of vulnerabilities that are found.

The "Vulnerability Analysis" component abstractly defines all of the targeted vulnerability finders. For example, a re-entrancy bug detector may perform additional analysis if an external function call is detected. An analyzer searching for timestamp dependencies may check if any traces have conditionals that depend on the block's timestamp. Integer overflow detectors hone in on arithmetic expressions, checking if the result can exceed the maximum value of the numeric type. We'll look deeper into a few examples in the following section.

Finally, many analyzers include a "Validation" step, which attempts to ensure that the found exploits can actually be realized through explicit transactions. This may involve spinning up a test network and issuing transactions to ensure that the faulty behavior occurs. This helps to avoid some false positives.

Different properties of analyzers and their underlying infrastructure determine the types of vulnerabilities that can be discovered. An analyzer is said to be *intraprocedural* if it only considers logical paths through a single function at a time, abstracting away other functions and calls to external contracts. As we will see in the following sections, this is sufficient for detecting certain kinds of re-entrancy attacks, such as that in the DAO exploit [104]. An analyzer is *inter-procedural* if the analyzer follows the execution of function calls, rather than symbolically abstracting away their behavior (which may introduce false positives). Sequences of function calls or *traces* can also be analyzed, which is often necessary to detect certain exploits, such as the Parity bug [105]. Note that inter-procedural analysis does not necessarily imply that all calls to other functions will be followed, particularly as this is not possible if the called contract is not known in advance.

5.3.3 EXAMPLE ANALYSES

Here, we'll discuss how symbolic analyzers can be useful to detect common vulnerabilities using our running example in Figure 5.2.

5.3.3.1 Finding Re-Entrancy Attacks with Symbolic Analysis

Suppose we wish to determine whether the `guess` function in Figure 5.2 is susceptible to a re-entrancy attack. As with any re-entrancy exploit, in order for this to happen `guess` must call some external function which in turn calls `guess` again before the relevant state variables have been updated, potentially taking more funds than was intended by the smart contract. In order for this to occur, we must first check if the external function call on Line 35 can be reached, which amounts to checking the following constraints[2]:

$$
\begin{aligned}
&\texttt{msg.sender != owner \&\& msg.value == 1 ether} \\
&\texttt{\&\& transformed\_answer = answer * multiplier} \\
&\texttt{\&\& !locked \&\& reward == this.balance \&\&} \\
&\texttt{transformed\_answer < answer}
\end{aligned} \tag{5.1}
$$

The first five constraints are easily satisfied by having a transaction with 1 ether sent from any address other than the owner. In order to satisfy the final constraint *transformed_answer* < *answer*, we can exploit the fact

---

[2] Additional constraints are needed to update the value of `reward` on Line 25, however the most straightforward encoding of the constraint: *reward* == *reward* + *value* presents a problem: the only way to satisfy this constraint is if *value* = 0. In order to encode variable updates, the notion of *static single assignment (SSA) form* is used to disambiguate the variable's value before and after the assignment by introducing fresh logical variables [106]. In our example, the assignment would instead be encoded as $reward_1 == reward_0 + value$, where $reward_0$ and $reward_1$ are fresh variables.

that SafeMath was not used for multiplication, and set *answer* to any value above 2^{251} due to integer overflow in the expression *answer ∗ multiplier*.

At this point, the analyzer has a path constraint indicating all conditions that must hold in order for a single external call to occur. However, the reachability of the external call alone is not enough to suggest a re-entrancy vulnerability. The analyzer can then check whether the call can be reached again by checking whether the path constraint still holds after all state variables have been updated from the first call. In this example, since the only state variable that is updated is *reward_pool*, the constraints are still satisfiable through the same reasoning as previously mentioned. This suggests that the function can indeed be exploited through a re-entrancy attack. In this case, the function can repeatedly be invoked draining half the remaining ether upon each call. The Oyente analyzer checks for re-entrancy using this approach [94].

Now, suppose we fix the vulnerability in `guess` by moving the assignment *locked = true* before the external function call. When the analyzer attempts to find an assignment to variables that allows a re-entrant call, it quickly determines that this is impossible, since after the first call we have the constraint *locked == true* (due to the assignment now being along the path of statements from the start of the function to the external call), and in order to reach the call the second time, we must have that *locked == false*. The underlying SMT solver determines that these two constraints are contradictory, indicating that we've successfully patched the vulnerability.

The Mythril analyzer takes an even stricter approach than Oyente when detecting re-entrancy. Rather than determining if the external function call can be reached again after the first invocation (as in Oyente), Mythril checks whether any state changes (for example, state variable assignments) can occur after an external call, and if so, a re-entrancy warning is emitted. This is in the spirit of the design pattern that recommends updating all state variables prior to external calls.

5.3.3.2 *Detecting the Parity Bug with Inter-Procedural Analysis*

The re-entrancy attack as shown earlier only required analyzing the single function `guess` in order to find the exploit. However, certain vulnerabilities may require a sequence of function calls. As discussed in Chapter 4, the Parity bug involved a malicious user first acquiring ownership of the contract through an unprotected function, and then invoking a `kill` function rendering the contract useless. As can be seen in Figure 5.2, a similar exploit exists in `Puzzle` by invoking `set_owner` followed by `destroy_puzzle`. Although intuitively very simple, this bug cannot be discovered by intra-procedural analyzers as the exploit requires two function calls.

In order to check whether the Parity bug exists, an inter-procedural analyzer may first check whether the operation `selfdestruct` exists anywhere in the smart contract. If so, the analyzer performs a depth-first search over all functions that can be invoked externally, up to some depth limit, with the goal of invoking the `selfdestruct` operation as an address other than the owner. The global state is maintained in-between calls along the same trace, and paths within functions are analyzed as within an intra-procedural analyzer. The Maian analyzer [95] builds on top of Oyente by supporting inter-procedural sequences or "traces" of function calls. With this approach, Maian is able to detect the Parity bug in our Puzzle contract with a trace invoking `set_owner` followed by `destroy_puzzle`.

5.3.3.3 Other Analyses

Most intra-procedural smart contract analyzers support many of the same vulnerability types. Integer overflow and underflow are detected by checking whether integer expressions can exceed the maximum integer value, or go below zero. In our running example, the expression *answer * multiplier* triggers a warning, since any value to *answer* above 2^{251} will cause an overflow. If SafeMath were used such that the expression was changed to *answer.mul(multiplier)*, an assertion statement would be included before the actual multiplication occurs, removing the possibility of overflow.

As another example, *timestamp dependence*, in which conditional paths through a function require comparison to the block's timestamp, should generally be avoided when possible, as the miner may manipulate the timestamp in order to change the result of the transaction. Given a path conditional corresponding to some trace through the contract (as constructed by the CFG building phase), the analyzer can simply check if the block's timestamp is involved in any expression within the conditional. Note that this check does not require invoking the SMT solver.

Maian supports three main classes of trace bugs. The first looks for traces that allow an unprivileged user to invoke a `selfdestruct` operation, as in the previously described Parity bug. Mythril has also added support for this type of vulnerability. The second are called "prodigal bugs," in which an arbitrary user who has never interacted with the smart contract is able to take ether. These two types of vulnerabilities are categorized as *safety properties*—properties that ensure that no "bad event" will ever happen. The third are called "greedy bugs," which characterize contracts that have no way of releasing ether, that is, there is a non-zero ether balance which is locked in the contract forever. This is considered a *liveness property*, which ensures that something "good" will eventually happen.

5.3.4 NO SILVER BULLET AFTER ALL

Most of these analyzers allow for "push-button" fully-automated analysis—just pass your code into the tool, and it'll take care of the rest! Simple, right?

Unfortunately, full automation comes at a price: checking non-trivial semantic properties of programs is, in general, an *undecidable problem* [107], that is, it is impossible to create an algorithm which can correctly decide whether the property holds for any given input program. These analyzers, therefore, rely upon creating abstractions or restrictions on the analysis, in order to provide meaningful results most of the time. Consider Figure 5.5. Errors come in two primary types. False positives occur when the analyzer asserts that a vulnerability or issue exists in the program, when in actuality the program is correct. False negatives occur when a vulnerability or issue exists in the program but the analyzer fails to detect it.

Each of the aforementioned tools generate both false positives and false negatives, and while many of these errors are intrinsic to the analyses being performed, others are due to design decisions of the tools. Let's take a look at some issues that may occur from the results of these analyzers. We note that these tools are still being actively developed, and behavior may change in future releases.[3]

False Positives. The primary source of false positives comes from either lacking information about the surrounding environment of a smart contract (for example, external calls to other contracts), or engineering design choices in the analyzer that flag benign issues in the code. For example, Mythril flags the statement `reward += msg.value;` as a source of potential integer overflow. In order for this to actually occur though, the

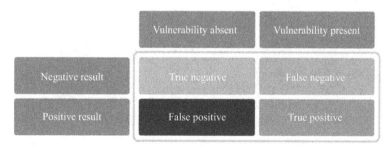

Figure 5.5. Possible results from an analyzer. A good analyzer should strive to maximize true positives while minimizing false positives.

---

[3] At the time of writing, we used Oyente v0.2.7 and Mythril v0.18.9. Maian does not have explicit versioning, however we used the tool at commit sha `ab387e171b-f99969676e60a0e5c59de80af15010` from their repository [108].

sender would need to have on the order of 2^{256} ether, which would indicate much bigger problems than these analyzers attempt to address. Nonetheless, using SafeMath as a habit for any arithmetic is not a bad idea, regardless of the likelihood of exploits.

As an example of how environment abstractions can lead to false positives, consider the following simple contracts in Figure 5.6. The Main contract gets initialized by taking the address of the Helper contract. Assuming the contracts are deployed correctly, such that address passed to Main's constructor points to the Helper contract, the conditional in the withdraw function can never be satisfied. Thus, the re-entrancy issue we've seen many times before cannot actually take place, since the lines of code are effectively dead. However, since the analyzers do not assume correct initialization, the external call to external.always_false() is replaced with a symbolic value that can take on any value (for example, true), and re-entrancy vulnerabilities are reported.

Bounds on the search space may also induce false positives. Consider Figure 5.7. In this contract, ether can only be sent to a destination address on Line 12 if the majority of contract owners confirm the transaction, which is abstracted away as the isConfirmed(tId) call on Line 9. Suppose there are seven owners of the contract and at least four of them must confirm a transaction. Then a trace of the contract that sends ether must include at least 6 transactions: one to create the proposed transaction,

```
1  contract Helper {
2      function Helper(){}
3
4      function always_false() returns(bool){
5          return false;
6      }
7  }
8
9  contract Main {
10     Helper helper;
11     mapping(address => uint256) public balance;
12
13     function Main(address addr){
14         helper = Helper(addr);
15     }
16
17     // omitting other functions such as a payable
18
19     function withdraw() {
20         if(helper.always_false()){
21             msg.sender.call.value(balance[msg.sender])();
22             balance[msg.sender] = 0;
23         }
24     }
25 }
```

Figure 5.6. A contract that calls a known external function.

```
1   function confirmTransaction(uint tId)
2       ownerExists(msg.sender) {
3       confirmations[tId][msg.sender] = true;
4       executeTransaction(tId);
5   }
6
7   function executeTransaction(uint tId) {
8       // In case of majority
9       if (isConfirmed(tId)) {
10          Transaction tx = transactions[tId];
11          tx.executed = true;
12          if (tx.destination.call.value(tx.value)(tx.data))
13              /*....*/
14  }}
```

Figure 5.7. A contract that may incorrectly be flagged as greedy by Maian, due to the bounded search space. Originally described in [95].

four approvals from owners, and one to actually execute the transaction. Since Maian by default only considers traces of length two, this contract will be flagged as greedy, since it cannot find a sequence of at most two transactions that lead to the ether transfer. Increasing the trace length can allow Maian to determine that the contract is not greedy.

False Negatives. Even if an analyzer claims to handle certain classes of vulnerabilities, there is often no guarantee that all issues will be found. This most commonly is due to two reasons: (1) engineering choices limit its ability to find bugs in certain cases, and (2) the search space of possible paths through the contract was not fully explored due to the state explosion problem.

As an example limitation, suppose we make a simple change to our Puzzle contract by removing the constant modifier on multiplier. Although a seemingly benign change (particularly since no function even exists to change the variable), Oyente can no longer detect that a re-entrancy attack is possible, nor does it detect the transaction-ordering dependence between calls to guess and destroy_puzzle. Further, Mythril can no longer detect an integer overflow in the expression *answer * multiplier*. Unfortunately, understanding why this limitation exists would require exploring the deeper nuances of how these tools were engineered, but the example is a reminder that these tools cannot offer guarantees of the correctness of code.

It's important to keep in mind that most of these tools are still in early stages of development, and may have bugs of their own, limiting their ability to find vulnerabilities. Beyond that, without deep knowledge of the smart contract being analyzed, it is often unclear how parameters such as the max call depth should be set. Analyzers come with reasonable default values which work in the typical case, but this may not be sufficient for all contracts. Further, underlying nuances of the analyzer may cause certain vulnerabilities to be missed even in seemingly simple cases.

This is not to say that these analyzers are not useful—they are incredibly important for ensuring correctness of smart contracts; just don't treat their results as gospel. Ultimately, it is in the hands of you (and end-users of your smart contract) to ensure that no security vulnerabilities exist.

5.4   SECURIFY

Each of the aforementioned analyzers follow the same main paradigm of symbolic execution: contracts are symbolically traced, and the satisfiability of path conditions along with other vulnerability-specific constraints is used to detect exploits. These approaches suffer from two main weaknesses: first, they are neither sound (false positives exist) nor complete (false negatives exist); and second, they are not easily extended to new, possibly contract-specific analyses. For example, suppose the contract writer wishes to check whether a specific function call is restricted to being called by a specific address (for example, it is an *onlyOwner* function), rather than an arbitrary address. Since the symbolic analyzers, shown earlier, only check for globally problematic patterns such as reentrancy bugs, there is no easy way to ensure this type of contract-specific property with those tools.

Securify [116] aims at addressing both of these issues. In order to construct contract specific property checks, Securify defines a domain-specific language (DSL) to define code patterns that correspond to these properties. Common analyses such as re-entrancy detection are also encoded with this language. Securify takes a smart contract and a set of patterns as input, and determines whether the code is compliant or violates any of the given patterns. Securify distinguishes whether the code definitely violates a pattern, or if the analysis is incomplete (that is, the tool cannot verify whether the code complies with or violates a pattern), then a warning is provided as output instead. While this does not completely eliminate the issue of false positives and false negatives, it is a step in the right direction, as other tools typically only output warnings, not guaranteeing the correctness of any of its results. If most of the output of Securify is definite violations of the patterns, this reduces the amount of output that must be manually verified by the user.

Unlike the previously discussed tools, Securify does not use a typical symbolic execution approach to reason about smart contracts, but instead works as follows. Consider Figure 5.8, which includes an annotated

```
1  function abbreviated_guess(uint256 answer) payable{
2      ...
3      if (transformed_answer < answer){
4          reward_pool -= reward; // L1
5          msg.sender.call.value(reward)(); // L2
6          locked = true; // L3
7      }
8  }
```

```
1  Base Facts:
2  Store(L1, reward_pool, reward_pool - reward)
3  Call(L2, 'call args')
4  Store(L3, locked, true)
5  Follow(L1, L2)
6  Follow(L2, L3)
7
8  Inferred Facts:
9  MayFollow(L1, L2)
10 MustFollow(L1, L2)
11 MayFollow(L2, L3)
12 MayFollow(L1, L3)
13 MustFollow(L2, L3)
14 MustFollow(L1, L3)
```

Property	Type	Pattern
No writes after call	Compliance violation	all $Call(L_{i\prime}\ \_)$: all $Store(L_{j\prime\_\prime}\_)$: $MayFollow(L_i, L_j)$ some $Call(L_{i\prime}\ \_)$: some $Store(L_{j\prime\_\prime}\_)$: $MustFollow\ (L_i, L_j)$

Figure 5.8. Shortened version of the guess function from Figure 5.2. Lines are commented with tags inferred by Securify. Only facts relevant to the re-entrancy bug detection are listed; in general, each line would include many more inferred facts. The patterns for no writes after call is listed below (adopted from [116]).

version of our guess function from Figure 5.2.[4] We will use this example to describe how re-entrancy vulnerabilities can be detected.

Given EVM bytecode, Securify first decompiles the code into a single static assignment (SSA) representation (see Footnote 2), and assigns a unique label L_s to each statement s of decompiled code. Lines are tagged with *semantic facts*, which describe properties about the line and are used for reasoning about security patterns. The tagging process initially assigns *base facts*, which are primarily two types: instruction-type facts and basic control flow facts. Instruction facts simply describe the operation that occurs in the statement. For example, the assignment to the state variable *locked* on Line 6 is annotated with the tag $Store(L_3, locked, true)$. The tag

---

[4] Although Securify works at the bytecode level, we abstract to the source-code level to keep the explanation more intuitive.

Follow is used to indicate instructions that are consecutively executed; for example, the line tagged L_1 is directly after L_2, and is therefore tagged *Follow*(L_1, L_2). Although not depicted in our example, `Join` and `Goto` tags are used to describe control flow in the case of conditional branching.

Next, *inferred facts* are derived from base facts using a set of semantic rules. For example, the fact *MayFollow* is derived with the following two rules:

$$MayFollow(L_i, L_j) \leftarrow Follow(L_i, L_j)$$

$$MayFollow(L_i, L_j) \leftarrow MayFollow(L_i, L_k), Follow(L_k, L_j) \quad (5.2)$$

Intuitively, any instruction that *may* occur after another instruction during execution will be tagged with *MayFollow* accordingly. Rules to derive inferred facts are applied recursively. As an example, since *Follow*(L_1, L_2) is a base fact in Figure 5.8, from the first rule we know that *MayFollow*(L_1, L_2) must be true. Applying the second rule with base fact *Follow*(L_2, L_3) and newly inferred fact *MayFollow*(L_1, L_2), we can derive *MayFollow*(L_1, L_3). The *MustFollow* tag is inferred similarly, however, statements that are not guaranteed to follow (due to branching) will not receive the tag. Although in our example every *MayFollow* tag has a corresponding *MustFollow* tag, a function that contains branches will, in general, have fewer *MustFollow* tags than *MayFollow*. Inferred facts are automatically derived using an underlying stratified Datalog system [115], which requires as input inference rules and base facts. Other facts, such as those related to data dependencies are also considered in Securify— however, we will omit them from our example.

Once we have saturated the system with all possible inferred facts, vulnerability-specific patterns can be checked to determine any issues with the code. The rule for *no writes after call* is listed in Figure 5.8. As discussed earlier in Figure 5.1, this pattern should be avoided as it is often susceptible to re-entrancy attacks. The compliance pattern can be interpreted as: "for every call instruction labeled L_i and store instruction labeled L_j, L_j may not follow L_i." The '_' terms denote that the pattern does not care about the values of the parameters. If this pattern holds, then we know that regardless of the path taken by the program, a store instruction will never follow a call instruction. The violation pattern conversely states that there exists some call instruction L_i and store instruction L_j in the program such that the L_j must follow L_i. In our running example, we can see that `guess` violates this pattern by letting $L_i = L_2$ and $L_j = L_3$.

In general, Securify is able to detect many of the same vulnerabilities as Oyente and Mythril using this pattern-based approach. The pattern based approach also readily extends to contract specific analyses, which may be useful for checking requirements specific to a given project. As another advantage, its approach can often *guarantee* that a pattern is violated/conformed to by the smart contract, mitigating some of the manual checking required by the user. The tool does come with some limitations, however. First, it assumes that all program statements are reachable, that is, there is no dead code. To see how this is a problem, suppose that the constraints in our guess function were unsatisfiable, and therefore no possible input could execute the store and call statements that led to re-entrancy. Since the tool does not check whether these lines can be reached, the tool will still flag a re-entrancy attack even though it is no longer possible. Second, the analyzer does not robustly handle arithmetic constraints, which is a strongpoint of the underlying SMT solvers found in symbolic analyzers. Both of these limitations may suggest a hybrid approach that combines the reachability and numerical analysis benefits of the symbolic analyzer with the pattern-based matching present in Securify.

5.4.1 ANALYZER OVERVIEW

The previous two sections discussed several of the most commonly used smart contract analyzers in practice. However, this is a rapidly developing field and several other tools are already available or will soon be. The Manticore symbolic analyzer supports many of the same analyses as shown previously, such as re-entrancy and overflow detection. It also supports custom analyses through a Python interface. The Zeus analyzer [110] claims to have zero false negatives through an approach that compiles EVM bytecode and constraints to LLVM bytecode, which can be processed by the LLVM static analyzer [109]. The CertiK platform [112] translates code to kEVM [111], a formally verified version of the EVM semantics in K [113] (discussed briefly in Chapter 2). Custom analyses are supported, but must be written as pre-conditions and post-conditions for the functions under analysis.

Table 5.1 summarizes the supported analyses of each of the four discussed analyzers. Even though there is an overlap in the analyses supported by Oyente, Mythril, and Securify, it is often valuable to run all tools available. Since these tools have a significantly different implementation, there is no guarantee that they will find the same vulnerabilities.

Table 5.1. Summary of analyses supported by open-source smart contract analyzers

	Oyente	Mythril	Securify	Maian
Integer overflow/underflow	Yes	Yes		
Re-entrancy	Yes	Yes	Yes	
Transaction-ordering dependence	Yes	Yes	Yes	
Timestamp dependence	Yes	Yes	Yes	
Callstack depth attack	Yes	Yes	Yes	
Parity bug	Yes	Yes	Yes	
Unchecked self destruct				Yes
Prodigal				Yes
Locked ether			Yes	Yes

5.5 AUDITS

Working on a dApp that has the potential to reach a significant number of users? Already familiar with the aforementioned tools and best practices? Great! Chances are, there's still some room for improvement in the code. Smart contract development is a notoriously tricky domain, and even the most seasoned veterans in the space can miss vulnerabilities, possibly leading to significant financial impact [104, 105]. In many cases, it's best to get a fresh set of eyes on the code to ensure that it is indeed correct.

Several smart contract professional auditing companies, such as Quantstamp, Chain-Security, ConsenSys, and Trail Of Bits, provide manual audits of smart contracts through trained security experts. These auditors are trained to reason about complex smart contract code, use tools and analyzers to inspect for vulnerabilities, and ensure that the code generally behaves as expected. As part of the audit process, a report is typically created to describe any issues that were discovered during the audit. The use of this report is twofold. First, the requestor of the audit can take action to address any concerns described in the report. Second, the report can be used to bolster confidence in the correctness of the product not only for the contract writer, but also end-users who wish to actually interact with the smart contract. In some sense, the report demonstrates to the general public that the contract writer has done their due diligence to ensure correctness of their product.

In order to effectively assess your smart contract, auditors require more than just the code. Without proper documentation, the auditor can only infer the intended semantics of the code, and cannot properly assess the correctness of the contract's behavior. In general, a set of guidelines is available at [13], which outlines the main steps and requirements of a typical audit. In Figure 5.9, we only highlight the main requirements.

- Prepare documentation regarding the intended behavior of the smart contract. This is typically in the form of either a whitepaper and/or a requirements/specification document.
- Provide the source code and surrounding project artifacts (for example, the test suite).
- Specify special requirements within your contract, such as compiler information, custom code used, and non-standard language practices.
- Identify any other special requirements for the audit, such as confidentiality requirements.
- Identify the target date of your audit completion.
- Be prepared for back and forth communication with the auditors.

Figure 5.9. Checklist for preparing a smart contract for audit. Further steps and details are available at [13].

First, documentation should be prepared as discussed in Section 5.1.3. Correctness can only be checked if the behavior has been clearly and explicitly documented—auditors can't [always] read minds! Ideally, documentation such as requirements or specification documents should be prepared long before the auditing phase of smart contract development.

Second, a code package should be prepared for the audit, which includes not only the source code, but also other project artifacts such as deployment scripts and unit tests. In many cases, this takes the form of a `truffle` project along with a detailed README file indicating how to deploy or run tests. Smart contracts should include detailed comments; functions should have comment blocks indicating the intended behavior of the code, as well as descriptions of the input and output variables. Unit tests are typically evaluated for coverage; program lines or control-flow paths which are not tested could indicate oversights during development which should be considered further. In most cases, 100 percent code coverage is recommended (excluding standard library contracts which the project depends upon).

Third, if the smart contract intentionally goes against standard practices for project-specific reasons, this should be articulated to the auditors. For example, some projects may choose to avoid using require statements in favor of if-conditionals which emit an event prior to returning. This is useful if another component of the dApp requires feedback in the form of events in the case of errors. As another example, if the testing environment differs significantly from a typical setup (that is, a `truffle` project with associated unit tests), additional notes should be specified as to how the developers evaluate their testing framework, particularly in terms of coverage.

The remaining steps involve being open with the auditors regarding the logistics of the audit. For example, if the smart contract is quite complex, it is unlikely that a meaningful audit could be performed in a few days. While common contracts such as those related to token sales can often be audited in a few days, the most elaborate audits can take up to weeks at a time. Finally, it is important to be available for communication with auditors; it is often the case that clarifications are needed if the requirements seem underspecified, or parts of the code are unclear or not aligned with the requirements.

5.5.1 CROWDSALE AUDITS

Crowdsale and token contracts are one of the most common types of smart contracts, and due to the amount of financial stake involved, they are also some of the most common to be audited. In Figure 5.10, we discuss some crowdsale-specific considerations to use as a guide for running a successful crowdsale.

- Is your token mintable and/or burnable?
- Will there be an address management system (that is, a whitelisting/blacklisting system)?
- What are the token caps and prices? Are prices adjusted during the sale?
- Is 2-factor authentication (2FA) used to secure wallets/websites/email accounts/and so on?

Figure 5.10. Checklist for preparing a crowdsale smart contract. Further steps and details are available at [13].

Different functionalities of tokens must be considered when designing the economics of your token. Mintable tokens can be created after the initial crowdsale, whereas the entire supply of non-mintable tokens are created when the token contract is deployed. Burnable tokens allow users to destroy owned tokens, reducing the overall supply. A common use-case of burnable tokens is to reduce surplus tokens after a crowdsale, such that the developers receive a pre-specified fraction of the total tokens. Each of these options should be thoughtfully considered prior to audit.

Second, it should be considered whether address whitelisting will be required for the crowdsale. In this case, only pre-approved addresses will be allowed to purchase tokens, often with a specified purchase cap. This helps to prevent participants from purchasing disproportionate amounts of tokens (sometimes called "whales"), which may undermine the economic model of the token. Regulatory bodies may even require whitelisting for certain countries, such that only specific types of investors would be allowed to purchase tokens. This may require additional infrastructure beyond the smart contract, such as ID whitelisting and management systems.

Third, it must be determined up front how much tokens will cost (typically in terms of ether values). This is largely determined based on community demand of the token. As a further incentivizing component, crowdsales often have a configurable bonus values given to users who invest early, essentially "jumpstarting" the crowd-sale. Users who come to the crowdsale later will typically receive lower bonuses.

Perhaps most importantly, you should ensure that all surrounding infrastructure of the crowdsale is properly secured. All relevant devices, addresses, emails, and other components should be secured with 2-factor authentication. Employees and community members should be cognizant of various security threats, such as phishing attacks which may compromise the system.

5.6   GUIDELINES

There is no "one right way" to develop a secure smart contract. Nonetheless, best practices can mitigate the chance of issues. In this chapter, we walked through fundamental approaches to mitigate security issues in smart contract development. The following checklist in Figure 5.11 should serve as a guide and a reminder of key steps that should be taken during development.

- Avoid common vulnerabilities by following best-practices and common design patterns as suggested in Figure 5.1.
- Properly document the code, ensuring that every function, along with its arguments and return value, is meaningfully described.
- Create unit and end-to-end tests. Ideally, the code and path coverage should be close to 100 percent (however high coverage does not necessarily indicate a good test suite).

- Run available smart contract analyzers, and address any flagged issues.
- Ensure that the infrastructure surrounding your dApp is properly secured, and 2-factor authentication is used throughout.
- Keep up-to-date on newly discovered vulnerabilities.
- If you're working on a project that has potentially very high valuation or is quite complex, it may be worth getting a second opinion on the security of the smart contract in the form of an audit.

Figure 5.11. Primary guidelines for smart contract development.

CHAPTER 6

CONCLUSION

6.1 SECURITY IS A BUSINESS STRATEGY, NOT JUST A TECHNICAL CHALLENGE

For any successful venture in blockchain, security should be a fundamental pillar of that company's success, because the goal of this technology is to eventually be used easily and safely by millions of people. As we see in the wider world outside of blockchain with the Facebook and Equifax data breaches, trust is easily lost, and not easily regained. For companies attempting to build the next killer app, trust is a precious resource to nurture and protect.

While this book focuses on the technology, protocols, and tools, thinking about security as only a technology challenge would be a disservice. To address smart contract security challenges, it is important to embed prudent business practices throughout your team and organization.

6.2 APPLYING AN ITERATIVE APPROACH TO SECURITY

Smart contracts are still very new. We can expect constant changes in the technology, solutions, and security landscape. New bugs and security risks are constantly being discovered and new best practices will emerge over time. As illustrated in this book, the cost of failure can be high. Implementing changes can involve hard choices. Given this, we need to embrace an iterative approach to security.

1. Value simplicity when creating a smart contract. There is a time and place to take risks and be creative—but when it comes to smart contracts, consider following tested patterns and best practices to mitigate risks. Complex smart contracts increase the attack surface.

2. Writing proper documentation is key. Quality documentation helps your team understand how your smart contract is expected to behave and helps them stay up-to-date with where your smart contract stands in the development process. Documentation is a lifesaver for future team members and is critical for external auditors to perform their work.

3. Aim to catch bugs and vulnerabilities before they are published. Hire an independent auditor, especially for high-value smart contracts.

4. Failure and errors happen. If a vulnerability is discovered, make sure your team has a plan in place to quickly and efficiently upgrade your smart contract.

5. Stay up-to-date with this rapidly evolving field. It is crucial to be aware of the latest vulnerabilities, upgrades, and security techniques.

6. Visualization, static, and dynamic tools, and linters are improving rapidly. It is important to stay up-to-date with these tools as well.

6.3 SECURITY IS A HOLISTIC PROBLEM THAT INVOLVES PEOPLE, SYSTEMS AND PROCESSES

Security generally, not just smart contracts security, is increasingly important and complex. A security framework applies with three main components:

People Appropriate employee training and vetting is an important step. Companies need to consider both intentional and unintentional threats that may come from employees and team members. Create a security plan that includes educating your employees and team members about smart contract security. No amount of technology will help a company or a project when an employee or team members are not educated about best practices.

Unfortunately, some companies do not anticipate that threats may come from inside their organization or team. In fact, insider threats are a common risk and should be addressed in your security plan.

Systems Aside from adequate training and processes, technology is part of the front line of defense in the security battle. This book has detailed smart contract security options, development, and landscape. Of course, for the overall security of your business and project, you also need to stay current with other security risk mitigating technologies, such as network and application security.

Process Just having smart contract security experts working with your team may not be enough to ensure your safety. A security plan may be unsuccessful in its application without a well-planned process. It is a good idea to test your security plan often, create checkpoints with reviews and make adjustments based on the results you get from those tests.

6.4 BUILDING THE WORLD OF PROGRAMMABLE MONEY TOGETHER

We believe smart contracts and programmable money are key innovations and will bring forth a wave of change over the next decade. 10 years ago, the world was changed forever with the release of the first iPhone. What will the future look like in the next 10 years?

Our goal for the next 10 years is to help the first billion people use blockchain in a safe and secure manner. Massive changes will take place as new platforms are developed, new exploits are discovered, and the first million user dApps are released. We believe that adopting a strategic approach to this new wave is important for any business looking to capture market share and prevent being disrupted.

Gaining an understanding of this growing field will unlock an unprecedented potential for career growth for professionals across various industries. As new technologies develop, an understanding of how to work with these technologies will be a tremendous resource to draw on for those who invest the time to understand them.

At Quantstamp, we believe that the transition to an economy driven by smart contracts is inevitable. There are many opportunities for smart contracts to impact society and we are highly optimistic that use cases we have yet to think of will have a tremendous impact on how people transfer value and interact with each other in the future.

In 1994, it was difficult to imagine the impact the Internet would have on us today. Information was democratized and spread at an unprecedented rate throughout the world. Its impact can be compared to that of the printing press. We believe that blockchain and smart contract technology will have the same impact as these landmark technologies.

Although we believe smart contract adoption is inevitable, it is not guaranteed to happen anytime soon. In order for smart contracts to achieve mainstream adoption, users need to have confidence in the smart contracts they interact with. Unfortunately, it is currently unrealistic to expect users to have this confidence due to the multimillion dollars worth of cryptocurrency that has been lost or stolen from smart contracts written by leading developers in the field.

To some extent, this should be expected in this stage of development, but in order to move past this stage, we need to develop the necessary security practices to create secure smart contracts. This is what inspired the creation of this book; we want this book to be the foundation for upcoming smart contract developers. Through our experience auditing smart contracts, we have become well acquainted with the latest in smart contract security and best practices. If smart contracts are to succeed, this knowledge needs to be made widely available.

Although this book contains the latest information available, it should not be the last document you read concerning smart contract security. I will reemphasize the point that we are still in the infant stages of this rapidly evolving technology. In order to develop secure smart contracts, you must stay up-to-date with the latest findings in this field.

We're grateful to be in the middle of this rapidly developing industry, and thankful for the incredible support from around the world. We are excited to have you join us on this journey.

REFERENCES

[1] Botsman, R. n.d. "How the Blockchain is Redefining Trust." *Wired*, December 27, 2017. https://wired.com/story/how-the-blockchain-is-redefining-trust/ (accessed February 7,2019).

[2] Werbach, K., and N. Cornell. 2017. "Contracts Ex Machina." *Duke Law Journal* 67, p. 313.

[3] King of Ether. February 2016. "Post-Mortem Investigation." https://kingoftheether.com/postmortem.html (accessed October 2, 2018).

[4] Szabo, N. n.d. "Smart Contracts." http://fon.hum.uva.nl/rob/Courses/InformationInSpeech/CDROM/Literature/LOTwinterschool2006/szabo.best.vwh.net/smart_contracts_2.html (accessed October 28, 2018).

[5] Marr, B. n.d. "A Short History Of Bitcoin And Crypto Currency Everyone Should Read." *Forbes*, December 6, 2017. https://forbes.com/sites/bernardmarr/2017/12/06/a-short-history-of-bitcoin-and-crypto-currency-everyone-should-read (accessed February 7, 2019).

[6] Hertig, A. n.d. "How Do Ethereum Smart Contracts Work?" *CoinDesk*. https://coindesk.com/information/ethereum-smart-contracts-work

[7] ChainTrade. n.d. "10 Advantages of Using Smart Contracts." Last Modified December 26, 2017. https://medium.com/@ChainTrade/10-advantages-of-using-smart-contracts-bc29c508691a

[8] Mik, E. 2017. "Smart Contracts: Terminology, Technical Limitations and Real World Complexity." *Law, Innovation and Technology* 9, no. 2, pp. 269–300.

[9] Ream, J., Y. Chu, and D. Schatsky. 2016. "Upgrading Blockchains: Smart Contract Use Cases in Industry." *Deloitte Insights*, June 08, 2016. https://www2.deloitte.com/insights/us/en/focus/signals-for-strategists/using-blockchain-for-smart-contracts.html

[10] The Ethereum Wiki. n.d. "ERC20 Token Standard." https://theethereum.wiki/w/index.php/ERC20_Token_Standard (accessed October 29).

[11] Blockgeeks. 2018. "ERC20 Tokens: A Comprehensive Origin Story." https://blockgeeks.com/guides/erc20-tokens/ (accessed October 28, 2018).

[12] Investopedia. n.d. "Initial Coin Offering (ICO)." https://investopedia.com/terms/i/initial-coin-offering-ico.asp (accessed October 28, 2018).

[13] Smart Contract Security Alliance. n.d. "Standards for Smart Contract Security Audits." https://smartcontractsecurityalliance.com/ (accessed October 23, 2018).

[14] Hertig, A. n.d. "What is a DAO?" *CoinDesk*, https://coindesk.com/information/what-is-a-dao-ethereum (accessed October 12, 2018).

[15] CryptoKitties. n.d. "CryptoKitties: Collectible and Breedable Cats Empowered by Blockchain Technology." https://cryptokitties.co (accessed October 28, 2018).

[16] Nash, G. n.d. "The Anatomy of ERC721-Understanding Non-Fungible Tokens." *Medium*, December 23, 2017. https://medium.com/cryptocurrently/the-anatomy-of-erc721-e9db77abfc24

[17] Hertig, A. n.d. "What is a Decentralized Application?" *CoinDesk*, https://coindesk.com/information/what-is-a-decentralized-application-dapp (accessed October 11, 2018).

[18] Finley, K. n.d. "A $50 Million Hack Just Showed that the DAO was All Too Human." *Wired*, June 18, 2016. https://wired.com/2016/06/50-million-hack-just-showed-dao-human

[19] Aventinus, C. n.d. "Parity Multisig Wallet Hacked, or How Come?" *Coin Telegraph*, November 13, 2017. https://cointelegraph.com/news/parity-multisig-wallet-hacked-or-how-come

[20] Parity Technologies. "A Postmortem on the Parity Multi-Sig Library Self-Destruct." November 15, 2017. https://parity.io/a-postmortem-on-the-parity-multi-sig-library-self-destruct/ (accessed February 7, 2019).

[21] Town, S. n.d. "BatchOverflow Exploit Creates Trillions of Ethereum Tokens, Major Exchanges Halt ERC20 Deposits." *Crypto Slate*, April 25, 2018. https://cryptoslate.com/batchoverflowexploit-creates-trillions-of-ethereum-tokens

[22] Antonopoulos, A.M., and G. Wood. 2018. "Mastering Ethereum: Building Smart Contracts and Dapps." *O'Reilly*. https://github.com/ethereumbook/ethereumbook

[23] Ethereum. n.d. "Ethereum Whitepaper." https://github.com/ethereum/wiki/wiki/White-Paper (accessed October 9, 2018).

[24] Wood, G., and V. Buterin. n.d. "Ethereum: A Secure Decentralized Generalised Transaction Ledger." https://ethereum.github.io/yellowpaper/paper.pdf (accessed October 1, 2018).

[25] Hildenbrandt, E., M. Saxena, X. Zhu, N. Rodrigues, P. Daian, and D. Guth. 2017. "KEVM: A Complete Semantics of the Ethereum Virtual Machine."

[26] Grishchenko, I., M. Maffei, and C. Schneidewind. n.d. "EtherTrust: Sound Static Analysis of Ethereum Bytecode."

[27] Sipser, M. 1996. *Introduction to the Theory of Computation*. SIGACT News.

[28] Bertoni, G., J. Daemen, M. Peeters, and G.V. Assche. 2011. "The Keccak Reference." Last Modified January 14, 2011. https://keccak.team/files/Keccak-reference-3.0.pdf

[29] Dworkin, M.J. August 2015. "SHA-3 Standard: Permutation-Based Hash and Extendable-Output Functions." (No. Federal Inf. Process. Stds.(NIST FIPS)-202).

[30] Stack Exchange. n.d. "Which Cryptographic Hash Function Does Ethereum Use?" https://ethereum.stackexchange.com/questions/550/which-cryptographic-hashfunction-does-ethereum-use (accessed October 15, 2018).

[31] Hoffstein, J., J.C. Pipher, and J.H. Silverman. 2008. *An Introduction to Mathematical Cryptography, UTM,* 1 vols, New York, NY: Springer-Verlag.

[32] Accredited Standards Committee X9 Incorporated. 2005. "Public Key Cryptography for the Financial Services Industry, The Elliptic Curve Digital Signature Algorithm (ECDSA)." Accredited Standards Committee X9 Incorporated.

[33] Grishchenko, I., M. Maffei, and C. Schneidewind. 2018. "A Semantic Framework for the Security Analysis of Ethereum Smart Contracts." *Principles of Security and Trust,* 243–69, Springer, Cham.

[34] Luu, L., D.H. Chu, H. Olickel, P. Saxena, and A, Hobor. 2016. "Making Smart Contracts Smarter." *IACR Cryptology ePrint Archive 2016,* p. 633.

[35] GitHub. n.d. "Vyper." *Ethereum.* https://github.com/ethereum/vyper (accessed October 3, 2018).

[36] GitHub. n.d. "Solidity." *Ethereum.* https://github.com/ethereum/solidity (accessed September 29, 2018).

[37] Schrans, F. n.d. "Flint: A New Language for Safe Smart Contracts on Ethereum." April 15, 2018. https://medium.com/@fschrans/flint-a-new-language-for-safe-smart-contracts-onethereum-a5672137a5c7

[38] Breidenbach, L., I.C. Cornell Tech, P. Daian, F. Tramer, and A. Juels. August 2018. "Enter the Hydra: Towards Principled Bug Bounties and Exploit-Resistant Smart Contracts." In *27th USENIX Security Symposium (USENIX Security 18).* Baltimore, MD: USENIX Association.

[39] Daian, P. March, 2018. "RV Inc. & FSL @ UIUC to Formalize EthereumâĂˇZs Viper." https://runtimeverification.com/blog/rv-inc-fsl-uiuc-to-formalize-viper-language-and-compiler/ (accessed October 2, 2018).

[40] GitHub. n.d. "Semantics of Vyper in K." *Kframework.* Last Modified April 12, 2018. https://github.com/kframework/vyper-semantics/wiki (related to [19]).

[41] CryptoCompare. n.d. "Why is Ethereum Different to Bitcoin?" Last modified July 31, 2015. https://cryptocompare.com/coins/guides/why-is-ethereum-different-to-bitcoin/

[43] Readthedocs. n.d. "Vyper." https://vyper.readthedocs.io/en/latest/ (accessed October 11, 2018).

[44] Teutsch, J., and C. Reitwiebner. n.d. "A Scalable Verification Solution for Blockchains." November 16, 2017. https://people.cs.uchicago.edu/~teutsch/papers/truebit.pdf

[45] Cusce, C. n.d. "Ethereum Plasma–Part 2: How It Works." https://medium.com/@collin.cusce/why-business-needs-ethereum-plasmanow-how-it-works-key-components-pt-2-37a82737cd54 (accessed October 28, 2018).

[46] Poon, J., and V. Buterin. n.d. "Plasma: Scalable Autonomous Smart Contracts." https://plasma.io/plasma.pdf (accessed October 7, 2018).

[47] CryptoKitties. 2018. "CryptoKitties: Collectible and Breedable Cats Empowered by Blockchain Technology." https://cryptokitties.co/ (accessed October 28, 2018).

[48] King, S., and S. Nadal. n.d. "PPCoin: Peer-to-Peer Crypto-Currency with Proof-of-Stake." August 19, 2012. https://peercoin.net/whitepapers/peercoin-paper.pdf

[49] GitHub. n.d. "eip-20.md" *Ethereum*. Last Modified October 15, 2018. https://github.com/ethereum/EIPs/blob/master/EIPS/eip-20.md

[53] Buntinx, J.P. n.d. "What are Ethereum Uncles?" *The Merkle*, July 17, 2017. https://themerkle.com/what-are-ethereum-uncles/

[54] StackExchange. n.d. "What is the Exact 'Longest Chain' Rule Implemented in the Ethereum 'HomesteadâĂİ Protocol?" https://ethereum.stackexchange. com/questions/13378/what-is-the-exact-longest-chainrule-implemented-in-the-ethereum-homestead-p (accessed October 28, 2018).

[55] Ethereum Smart Contract Best Practices. n.d. "Recommendations for Smart Contract Security in Solidity." https://consensys.github.io/smart-contract-best-practices/recommendations/ (accessed October 28, 2018).

[56] Daian, P. n.d. "Solidity Anti-patterns: Fun with Inheritance DAG Abuse." *Phil Does Security*, https://pdaian.com/blog/solidity-anti-patterns-fun-with-inheritance-dagabuse (accessed June 11, 2018).

[57] Dean, J., and S. Ghemawat. 2004. "MapReduce: Simplified Data Processing on Large Clusters." *OSDI*.

[58] Teutsch, J., V. Buterin, and C. Brown. "Interactive Coin Offerings." https://people.cs.uchicago.edu/~teutsch/papers/ico.pdf (accessed December 17, 2017).

[59] Etherscan. n.d. "Etherscan Token Tracker." https://etherscan.io/tokens (accessed October 17, 2018).

[60] Buterin, V. n.d. "Analyzing Token Sale Models." June 9, 2017. https://vitalik.ca/general/2017/06/09/sales.html

[61] Learn Cryptography. https://learncryptography.com/cryptocurrency/51-attack

[62] BlockchainHub. n.d. "Blockchain Oracles." https://blockchainhub.net/blockchain-oracles/ (accessed October 4, 2018).

[63] Adler, J., R. Berryhill, A. Veneris, Z. Poulos, N. Veira, and A. Kastania. 2018. "ASTRAEA: A Decentralized Blockchain Oracle." https://arxiv.org/pdf/1808.00528.pdf (accessed August 1, 2018).

[64] Vogelstellar, F. n.d. "ERC: Token standard #20." https://github.com/ethereum/eips/issues/20 (Last Modified September 29, 2017).

[65] Antonopoulos, A.M., and G. Wood. n.d. "Mastering Ethereum." https://github.com/ethereumbook/ethereumbook (Last Modified October 21, 2018).

[66] Zeppelin. n.d. "Open Zeppelin." https://github.com/OpenZeppelin/openzeppelin-solidity (Last modified October 3, 2018).

[67] von Kleist, L. n.d. "Why ERC827 can Make you Vulnerable to Reentrancy Attacks and How to Prevent Them." https://medium.com/chainsecurity/why-erc827can-make-you-vulnerable-to-reentrancy-attacks-and-how-to-prevent-them-61aeb4beb6bf (accessed October 4, 2018).

[68] Lemble, A. n.d. "ERC827 Token Standard (ERC20 Extension) #827." https://github.com/ethereum/EIPs/issues/827 (Last Modified June 28, 2018).

[69] Bylica, P. n.d. "How to Find $10M Just by Reading the Blockchain." *Medium*, https://blog.golemproject.net/how-to-find-10m-by-just-reading-blockchain-6ae9d39fcd95 (accessed April 6, 2017).

[70] Solidity.readthedocs. n.d. "Common Patterns." https://solidity.readthedocs. io/en/v0.4.24/common-patterns.html (accessed October 16, 2018).

[71] Solidity.ReadtheDocs. 2018. "Security Considerations." https://solidity.read thedocs.io/en/develop/security-considerations.html (accessed October 1, 2018).

[72] Buterin, V. n.d. "Long-term Gas Cost Changes for IO-heavy Operations to Mitigate Transaction Spam Attacks #150." https://github.com/ethereum/ EIPs/issues/150 (Last Modified August 16, 2017).

[73] Parity Technologies. n.d. "The Multi-sig Hack: A PostMortem." https://par ity.io/the-multi-sig-hack-a-postmortem/ (accessed July 20, 2017).

[74] Etherscan. "The Address that Triggered the Parity Bug." https://etherscan.io/ address/0x863df6bfa4469f3ead0be8f9f2aae51c91a907b4 (accessed March 31, 2019).

[75] Solidity.ReadtheDocs. n.d. "Libraries." *Contracts*. https://solidity.readthed ocs.io/en/v0.4.25/contracts.html#libraries (accessed October 1, 2018).

[76] Bahrynovska, T. n.d. "History of Ethereum Security Vulnerabilities, Hacks, and their Fixes." https://applicature.com/blog/history-of-ethereum-securi ty-vulnerabilities-hacks-and-their-fixes (accessed September 27, 2017).

[77] ConsenSys. n.d. "Known Attacks." https://consensys.github.io/smart-con tract-best-practices/known_attacks (accessed October 23, 2018).

[78] ConsenSys. n.d. "Recommendations for Smart Contract Security in Solid ity." https://consensys.github.io/smart-contract-best-practices/recommenda tions (accessed October 1, 2018).

[79] Solidity.ReadtheDocs. n.d. "Application Binary Interface Specification." https://solidity.readthedocs.io/en/v0.4.25/abi-spec.html (accessed October 1, 2018).

[80] King of the Ether. n.d. "King of the Ether." https://kingoftheether.com/ thrones/kingoftheether/index.html (Last Modified May 25, 2017).

[81] Atzei, N., M. Bartoletti, and T. Cimoli. 2017. "A Survey of Attacks on Ethereum Smart Contracts SoK." In *Proceedings of the 6th International Conference on Principles of Security and Trust*, 164–86. https://eprint.iacr. org/2016/1007.pdf

[82] Humiston, P.E. n.d. "Smart Contract Attacks [Part 2]-Ponzi Games Gone Wrong." *Hackernoon*, https://hackernoon.com/smart-contract-attacks-part-2-ponzi-gamesgone-wrong-d5a8b1a98dd8 (accessed July 23, 2018).

[83] Toliuyi. n.d. "Alert! Will Fomo3D Destroy Ethereum?" https://ethresear.ch/t/ alert-will-fomo3d-destroy-ethereum/2630 (accessed November 23, 2018).

[84] Karalabe. n.d. "How to PWN FoMo3D, A Beginners Guide." https://reddit. com/r/ethereum/comments/916xni/how_to_pwn_fomo3d_a_beginners_ guide (accessed October 1, 2018).

[85] SECBIT. n.d. "How the Winner got Fomo3D prize-A Detailed Explanation." https://medium.com/coinmonks/how-the-winner-got-fomo3d-prize-a-detailedexplanation-b30a69b7813f (accessed October 3, 2018).

[86] SECBIT. n.d. "A Comprehensive Solution to Bugs in Fomo3D-like Games." https://hackernoon.com/a-comprehensive-solution-to-bugs-in-fomo3d-like-gamesab3b054f3cc5 (accessed October 10, 2018).

[87] Reutov, A. n.d. "Predicting Random Numbers in Ethereum Smart Contracts." https://blog.positive.com/predicting-random-numbers-in-ethereum-smart contracts-e5358c6b8620 (accessed October 1, 2018).

[88] Fomo3d. n.d. "Fomo3D Explained." https://fomo3d.hostedwiki.co/pages/ Fomo3D%20Explained (Last Modified August 07, 2018).

[89] ConsenSys. n.d. "Truffle Suite." https://truffleframework.com (accessed October 1, 2018).

[90] Protofire. n.d. "SolHint." https://protofire.github.io/solhint (accessed October 1, 2018).

[91] ConsenSys. n.d. "Ganache CLI." https://github.com/trufflesuite/ganache-cli (accessed October 1, 2018).

[92] OpenZeppelin. n.d. "OpenZeppelin-Solidity." https://github.com/OpenZeppelin/openzeppelin-solidity (accessed October 1, 2018).

[93] GitHub. 2018. "Solidity-Coverage." *Sc-forks*. https://github.com/sc-forks/solidity-coverage (accessed October 1, 2018).

[94] Luu, L., D.H. Chu, H. Olickel, P. Saxena, and A. Hobor. 2016. "Making Smart Contracts Smarter." *IACR Cryptology ePrint Archive 2016*, p. 633.

[95] Nikolic, I., K. Aashish, I. Sergey, P. Saxena, and A. Hobor. 2018. *Finding The Greedy, Prodigal, and Suicidal Contracts at Scale*. arXiv preprint arXiv:1802.06038.

[96] Mueller, B. 2018. *Smashing Ethereum Smart Contracts for Fun and Real Profit*. HITB SECCONF Amsterdam.

[97] De Moura, L., and N. BjÃÿrner. 2008. "Z3: An Efficient SMT Solver." In *International Conference on Tools and Algorithms for the Construction and Analysis of Systems*, 337–40. Berlin, Heidelberg: Springer.

[98] Wohrer, M., and U. Zdun. 2018. "Smart Contracts: Security Patterns in the Ethereum Ecosystem and Solidity." In *Blockchain Oriented Software Engineering* (IWBOSE), 2–8. International Workshop on, IEEE.

[99] ConsenSys. n.d. "Recommendations for Smart Contract Security in Solidity." https://consensys.github.io/smart-contract-best-practices/recommendations (accessed October 23, 2018).

[100] Solidity.readthedocs. n.d. "Function Modifiers." *Contracts*. https://solidity.readthedocs.io/en/develop/contracts.html#function-modifiers (accessed October 23, 2018).

[101] OpenZeppelin. n.d. "Pausable." https://github.com/OpenZeppelin/openzeppelin-solidity/blob/master/contracts/lifecycle/Pausable.sol (accessed October 23, 2018).

[102] OpenZeppelin. n.d. "SafeMath." https://github.com/OpenZeppelin/openzeppelin-solidity/blob/master/contracts/math/SafeMath.sol (accessed October 23, 2018).

[103] Inozemtseva, L., and R. Holmes. 2014. "Coverage is Not Strongly Correlated with Test Suite Effectiveness." In *Proceedings of the 36th International Conference on Software Engineering*, 435–45, 2014.

[104] Buterin, V. n.d. "CRITICAL UPDATE Re: DAO Vulnerability." https://blog.ethereum.org/2016/06/17/critical-update-re-dao-vulnerability/ (accessed October 23, 2018).

[105] Parity Technologies. n.d. "Anyone Can Kill your Contract." https://github.com/paritytech/parity-ethereum/issues/6995 (accessed October 23, 2018).

[106] Cytron, R., J. Ferrante, B.K. Rosen, M.N. Wegman, and F.K. Zadeck. 1991. "Efficiently Computing Static Single Assignment form and the Control Dependence Graph." *ACM Transactions on Programming Languages and Systems* (TOPLAS) 13, no. 4, pp. 451–90.

[107] Rice, H.G. 1953. "Classes of Recursively Enumerable Sets and their Decision Problems." *Transactions of the American Mathematical Society* 74, no. 2, pp. 358–66.

[108] "Maian." 2018. *MAIAN-tool.* https://github.com/MAIAN-tool/MAIAN (accessed October 23, 2018).

[109] Lattner, C., and V. Adve. 2004. "LLVM: A Compilation Framework for Lifelong Program Analysis and Transformation." In *Proceedings of the International Symposium on Code Generation and Optimization: Feedback-Directed and Runtime Optimization*, 75, IEEE Computer Society.

[110] Kalra, S., S. Goel, M. Dhawan, and S. Sharma. 2018. "Zeus: Analyzing Safety of Smart Contracts." *NDSS*.

[111] Hildenbrandt, E., M. Saxena, X. Zhu, N. Rodrigues, P. Daian, D. Guth, and G. Rosu. August 2017. "KEVM: A Complete Semantics of the Ethereum Virtual Machine." *The Journal of Logic and Algebraic Programming* 79, no. 6, pp. 397–434.

[112] "Certik." 2018. https://certik.org/ (accessed October 23, 2018).

[113] Rosu, G. n.d. "An Overview of the K Semantic Framework." *2018 IEEE 31st Computer Security Foundations Symposium (CSF)*. 10.1109/CSF.2018.00022

[114] Atlassian. n.d. "JIRA." https://atlassian.com/software/jira (accessed October 23, 2018).

[115] Ullman, J.D. 1984. *Principles of Database Systems*. Galgotia Publications.

[116] Tsankov, P., A. Dan, D.D. Cohen, A. Gervais, F. Buenzli, and M. Vechev. 2018. "Securify: Practical Security Analysis of Smart Contracts." *arXiv preprint arXiv:1806.01143*.

About the Authors

Richard Ma is the co-founder and CEO of Quantstamp. Prior to starting Quantstamp, Richard was a quantitative strategist and programmer in the algorithmic trading field, most recently with Tower Research Capital in San Francisco. Richard graduated with a degree in Electrical and Computer Engineering from Cornell University.

Jan Gorzny is a Blockchain Researcher for Quantstamp. He holds an MSc in mathematics from the University of Victoria and an MSc in computer science from the University of Toronto. Jan's role within Quantstamp is to keep up with emerging technologies, assist in protocol design, and develop ideas with the engineering team. His academic research interests include complexity theory, software verification and formal methods, and discrete mathematics.

Edward Zulkoski is a Senior Research Engineer at Quantstamp. He recently completed his PhD in Computer Science at the University of Waterloo with a focus on CDCL SAT solvers and SMT solvers, and holds a BS in Mathematics and Computer Science from Wilkes University.

Kacper Bak is a Senior Research Engineer at Quantstamp. He is an expert in software modeling and verification, and received PhD in Computer Science at the University of Waterloo for his work on modeling and analysis of software product lines. He has worked at MathWorks (MATLAB and Simulink), Opera Software, and Samsung.

Olga V. Mack is Vice President of Strategy at Quantstamp. Most recently, she served as General Counsel at ClearSlide and has worked at Visa, Zoosk, Wilson Sonsini, and Yahoo. She is an adjunct professor at Berkeley Law and earned both her JD and BA from UC Berkeley.

ABOUT THE CONTRIBUTORS

This book would not be possible without generous contributions from:

Martin Derka, PhD
Alex Murashkin, M Math
Nadir Akhtar
Leonardo Passos, PhD
Vajih Montaghami, PhD
Dan Zhang
Julian Martinez
Karina Crooks

INDEX

THIS TITLE IS FROM OUR COMPUTER ENGINEERING FOUNDATIONS, CURRENTS, AND TRAJECTORIES COLLECTION

Lisa MacLean, *Editor*

Momentum Press is one of the leading book publishers in the field of engineering, mathematics, health, and applied sciences. Momentum Press offers over 30 collections, including Aerospace, Biomedical, Civil, Environmental, Nanomaterials, Geotechnical, and many others.

Momentum Press is actively seeking collection editors as well as authors. For more information about becoming an MP author or collection editor, please visit http://www.momentumpress.net/contact

Announcing Digital Content Crafted by Librarians

Momentum Press offers digital content as authoritative treatments of advanced engineering topics by leaders in their field. Hosted on ebrary, MP provides practitioners, researchers, faculty, and students in engineering, science, and industry with innovative electronic content in sensors and controls engineering, advanced energy engineering, manufacturing, and materials science.

Momentum Press offers library-friendly terms:

- perpetual access for a one-time fee
- no subscriptions or access fees required
- unlimited concurrent usage permitted
- downloadable PDFs provided
- free MARC records included
- free trials

The **Momentum Press** digital library is very affordable, with no obligation to buy in future years.

For more information, please visit **www.momentumpress.net/library** or to set up a trial in the US, please contact **mpsales@globalepress.com**.